How Diesel & Electric Locomotives Work

JEFF WILSON

Kalmbach
Media

Thanks to all the photographers who contributed images to this project, especially the late J. David Ingles and Jim Wrinn — two friends and colleagues who provided a great deal of encouragement to me. I dearly wish both Dave and Jim could have seen this project in final form. Special thanks Cody Grivno and Brian Solomon, both of whom took the time to search their photo collections for photos and materials. Thanks also go to the public relations departments and company photographers at Electro-Motive, General Electric, and Alco, who did a marvelous job of documenting developments of early generations of diesels as their companies were introducing new models and innovations. And a hearty thanks to all of the photographers whose works reside at the David P. Morgan Memorial Library at Kalmbach Media. Those images, together with the library's significant collection of trade publications, journals, books, and manufacturers' manuals and materials, made this book possible.
— *Jeff Wilson, June 2023*

Kalmbach Media
21027 Crossroads Circle
Waukesha, Wisconsin 53186
www.KalmbachHobbyStore.com

Published in 2023
27 26 25 24 23   1 2 3 4 5

Manufactured in China

ISBN: 978-1-62700-945-4
EISBN: 978-1-62700-946-1

Editor: Bob Lettenberger
Book Design: Lisa Bergman

Library of Congress Control Number: 2023935056

On the cover: The engineer of Aberdeen Carolina & Western SD40-3 No. 6926 checks the locomotive's 645 engine before heading out on a run on June 4, 2014. *Steve Smedley*

Back cover, top left: Engineer Tony King is at the throttle of former Clinchfield F7 No. 800 on the CSX Santa Train in November 2017. *Ron Flanary* **Right:** Union Pacific employees change out engine power assemblies on an EMD SD40M-2 at the former Southern Pacific Roseville (Calif.) shops in 1996. *Steve Schmollinger* **Bottom left:** Shop forces at Metro East Industries in East St. Louis, Ill., wrap up rebuild and repaint work on Indiana Harbor Belt SW1500 No. 1512 in 2019. *Steve Smedley*

CONTENTS

Before the time of standardized locomotive offerings, diesels were a custom production. Union Pacific CD-05 (built in 1936 by EMC as M-10005) has a body from Pullman-Standard with automotive styling, a Winton Engine prime mover, and General Electric generators, control equipment and traction motors. The unit was assigned to the *City of Denver* streamliner. *EMD*

FROM DIESEL ENGINE TO TRACTION MOTOR

DIESEL-ELECTRIC LOCOMOTIVES ARE POWERFUL, COMPLEX, FASCINATING MACHINES

Along with the engine itself, an array of systems and other components work together delivering power to the rails and pulling trains. In the following pages, we'll trace these systems, starting with the diesel engine and working through the generator and traction motors, then look at fuel, oil, cooling systems, and various ancillary and control equipment.

Understanding how these locomotives work will give you a better appreciation for how they're designed, how and why they evolved, and why railroads use them the way they do. If you're a modeler, this understanding will help you figure out what the various details on models represent and what their functions are in real life.

It's important to understand that this book is not a spotter's guide — it's not designed to aid in identifying various models or manufacturers' distinct details. The photos and descriptions throughout cover more than 100 years of diesel production, and illustrate representative components from all major manufacturers and many individual models. It would be impossible to show and cite every variation regarding the many components and features.

Entire books and volumes have been written about the technical aspects of engines, generators, and other individual locomotive components. This book is not intended to do that. Instead, the goal is to explain how a locomotive's various features and systems work, using non-technical language that answers common questions — going into enough detail to provide a basic understanding of the technology.

We'll also show how the various components (and locomotives themselves) have evolved and grown in size and power since the early 1900s, with a look at horsepower, tractive effort, adhesion, and other operational factors.

There's also a chapter on electric locomotives, since they predated diesels and provided much of the groundwork for later diesel-electric development. We'll also review basic locomotive designs and body styles, providing brief histories of the major locomotive manufacturers.

This book focuses on road passenger

Workers lower a new SD40-2 body onto its trucks at EMD's assembly plant in La Grange, Ill., in January 1972. Diesel-electric locomotives house a number of systems that, working together, generate electricity, powering traction motors. The horsepower generated has moved trains for more than a century. *EMD*

and freight locomotives as well as switchers from major builders.

It does not cover small industrial diesels, turbines, or — other than brief summaries — genset or diesel-hydraulic locomotives.

My hope is that this book increases your knowledge and appreciation of diesel-electric locomotives. Turn the page and we'll take a quick look at the early history of diesel development, then we'll move into the literal nuts-and-bolts information with the engine itself.

CHAPTER 1

DIESEL-ELECTRIC EVOLUTION

Harnessing the internal-combustion engine — gas then diesel — put an end to the steam locomotive and revolutionized railroading

When Electro-Motive built E7 passenger diesel No. 504A (later renumbered 508) for Great Northern in June 1945, steam locomotives still outnumbered diesels 10-to-1. By the time of this 1967 photo, however, steam had been gone from U.S. and Canadian railroads for seven years. The streamlined, twin-engine E7, with 510 built, played a major role in bumping steam from passenger trains. *J. David Ingles*

The diesel-electric locomotive revolutionized railroading. The movement began with self-propelled gas-electric railcars in the 1910s and continued steadily, from the first boxcab diesel switchers of the 1920s to diesel streamliners of the 1930s and finally to heavy road freight locomotives of the 1940s. Diesels quickly proved their superiority in all types of service. The change from steam to diesel power was swift: Diesels accounted for less than 2% of the total locomotive fleet in 1940, but by 1960 steam was virtually gone from U.S. and Canadian railroads.

How did this happen, and why did railroads so quickly shift away from a technology that had been central to the industry for more than 120 years? The short answer is efficiency. However, getting to the point where diesel engines — and the locomotives they powered — could effectively replace steam locomotives took a few decades of experimentation.

Gasoline engines had been around since the 1870s, and their use in automobiles was growing rapidly by the turn of the 20th century. These engines were small, especially compared to the power output of a typical 1900 steam locomotive. Many developers did, however, see potential for possible railroad applications of the new technology.

Among the first rail uses of internal combustion was the railcar, basically a self-propelled passenger car that could provide passenger service on light-traffic branch and secondary lines. The McKeen Company produced its first in 1905. William R. McKeen developed the design with the backing of the Union Pacific's Edward H. Harriman, and McKeen sold more than 150 railcars through 1917. The cars presented a unique appearance with a knife-shaped prow and round side windows. Most had 100- or 200-hp gasoline engines, with some late cars having 300-hp engines.

Although the McKeen cars accomplished the goal of less-expensive operation compared to a steam-powered passenger train, they suffered from reliability problems.

TEXAS-MEXICAN DIESELS

The first Class I railroad in the U.S. to completely dieselize was the Texas-Mexican Railroad, a 160-mile long line in Texas that connects Loredo (a gateway to Mexico) and Corpus Christi, Texas.

The railroad bought seven Whitcomb double-ended, 70-ton, boxcab diesel-electrics built in 1939 (Nos. 501-507), allowing sale or retirement of its fleet of Ten-Wheeler steam locomotives. The diesels had four axles on a rigid frame and were powered by 660-hp Baldwin/De La Vergne engines (Baldwin owned Whitcomb) with Westinghouse electrical gear.

Whitcomb-built boxcab No. 502 switches on the Texas-Mexican Railway at Corpus Christi, Texas, in May 1941. *Jim Seacrest collection*

Most notably, the engine-drive system, which had the engine mounted on the lead truck directly driving the axles, was prone to stress-caused mechanical failures. Also, the transmission was difficult to manage, as reversing the car was a cumbersome process that required stopping the engine. Although distinctive and innovative, McKeen cars generally did not lead long lives.

A different type of transmission was needed, and the answer came from the technology of electric locomotives: using traction motors mounted on the trucks and axles, and having the railcar's engine drive a small generator to produce electricity to power the motors.

Credit for the first railcar using this method goes to General Electric, not surprising since the company had been active in building electric streetcars and railway equipment. In 1906 GE rebuilt a wood passenger car into a gas-electric car on the Delaware & Hudson. The company would become the most-successful of the early gas-electric railcar builders.

General Electric also gets credit for building the first true internal-combustion locomotive, a 350-hp, 57-ton, boxcab-style

McKeen railcars were the first widely produced self-propelled internal-combustion cars, using a gas-mechanical drive. They had distinctive pointed prows and round side windows. Union Pacific (Oregon-Washington Railroad & Navigation Co.) No. M-80, built in 1910, is at Moscow, Idaho, in July 1921.
W.T. Trebor

The Electro-Motive Corporation built the most-successful line of gas-electric railcars ("doodlebugs"). Burlington No. 9773 is at Peoria, Ill., in 1946. It has a Pullman body and a 275-hp Winton gasoline engine. Note the engine/generator visible through the cab door — operator safety and comfort were not priorities on early internal-combustion vehicles. *Louis A. Marre collection*

locomotive with two gasoline engines. It was built in 1913 for Minnesota's Dan Patch Lines, locomotive No. 100.

Technology evolved and reliability increased into the 1920s. Significant in 1923 was the formation of the Electro-Motive Co. (EMC, later Electro-Motive Corp.).

The company had a unique arrangement, as it had no manufacturing facility of its own. Instead, EMC contracted with the Winton Engine Co. for engines (gasoline or distillate), GE for electrical equipment, and a number of builders for the bodies, including Pullman and St. Louis Car Co. Electro-

Motive would become the industry's primary manufacturer of railcars, building more than 300 into the 1930s. Its products earned a reputation for reliability and durability.

A challenge for railcar and locomotive builders of this period was power. Gasoline engines were hitting their practical power limits at about 300 hp, and although distillate engines (more on their design in Chapter 2) could be larger and more powerful, they were maintenance intensive and suffered from reliability issues. The diesel engine was larger, more powerful, and burned cheaper fuel, but there were

Credit for the first internal-combustion locomotive goes to General Electric, which in 1913 built this 57-ton, two-engine, 350-hp gas-electric boxcab for Dan Patch Lines (Minneapolis, St. Paul, Rochester & Dubuque Electric Traction Co.) in Minnesota. The photo dates to 1915. *Navarro Fosse collection*

challenges to overcome to get a diesel to fit aboard a locomotive.

Diesel engines

The diesel engine is distinguished in that it doesn't require a spark to ignite the fuel in its cylinders. Instead, it relies on extreme heat caused by compressing air to burn the fuel. It is named for Rudolf Diesel, the German inventor who developed the design and built the first successful engine following the concepts in 1897. Continued development led to commercial engines by the early 1900s. By the 1910s, diesel engines were proving to work well in some applications, but they were large, heavy, and slow. The earliest successful diesel engines were used in ships or as stationary power plants in factories or generating stations.

Advantages of diesel engines included

heavier construction, required because of the increased cylinder pressure and higher temperatures compared to gas engines. This eventually led to higher reliability and longer lifespans, but engineers had to conquer problems related to metal stress and fatigue. Diesels also operated more efficiently than gasoline and other internal-combustion engines. They used cheaper fuel. Diesel fuel is safer to store and transport, as it has a higher flash point than gasoline and, although flammable, it is not explosive.

Improvements in diesel engine designs provided the impetus to make larger internal-combustion locomotives possible, but as Chapter 2 explains, it took time for the technology to improve to where engines were small enough — yet powerful and durable enough — to fit practically aboard a locomotive platform.

1953 AND 1960: LANDMARK YEARS FOR DIESEL EVOLUTION

1953

The year 1953 was notable in that it was the first year since 1828 that no U.S. railroad ordered a steam locomotive. That year, Norfolk & Western — the last major holdout to diesels — outshopped 0-8-0 switcher No. 244, the final steam product of its Roanoke Shops and the last reciprocating steam locomotive built for U.S. service. Diesel locomotives outnumbered steam for the first time, and diesels that year carried 74% of freight tonnage, 79% of all passenger trains, and did 83% of yard switching. Electro-Motive was the dominant builder, accounting for 73% of diesels in service; Alco had 15%, Fairbanks-Morse 7%, and Baldwin (including Lima-Hamilton) just 5%.

1960

Although a few steam locomotives remained serviceable on rosters and would run on a few short lines and industrial railroads in 1960, it was the year that dieselization effectively became complete. Several major Class I railroads operated steam for the final time, including Canadian National, Canadian Pacific, Duluth, Missabe & Iron Range, Grand Trunk Western, Illinois Central, and Norfolk & Western.

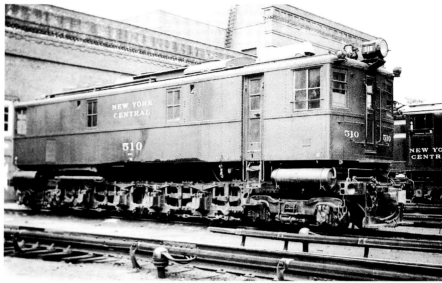

General Electric built this boxcab locomotive with Alco in 1923, featuring a six-cylinder Ingersoll-Rand diesel engine. It tested on several railroads through 1924 and 1925. *General Electric*

Alco-GE-IR built this 750-hp New York Central boxcab in 1928 with steam-style running gear: four-wheel leading and trailing trucks, with four driving axles (4-D-4 wheel arrangement). *Harold L. Goldsmith*

Early diesel-electric locomotives

From the 1910s to the 1920s, diesel locomotive development was spurred by smoke laws in New York and other large Eastern cities, where steam locomotives in urban areas were being pushed out. Railroads' options were electrifying lines — a costly proposition — or turning to internal combustion.

General Electric was again a pioneer, building the first true diesel-electric in 1917 using its own engine design, a small two-cylinder model (the GM-50). For a platform, GE used a steeple-cab electric body — the same type used on its interurban locomotive designs. The

company built three locomotives: for the Jay Street Connecting Railroad (Brooklyn), the City of Baltimore, and the U.S. Army. They were not successful, seeing limited service, and although GE abandoned its own engine design the company continued developing locomotives using engines from other sources. Most notably GE used a small Ingersoll-Rand four-cycle, six-cylinder diesel in a boxcab that tested on several railroads starting in 1924.

Steam builder Alco noticed the developments taking place with internal-combustion locomotives and railcars and decided to enter the field. To build its first diesel-electrics, Alco partnered with GE and Ingersoll-Rand (Alco had earlier worked with GE in building heavy electric locomotives). The Alco/GE/I-R consortium gets credit for building the first successful commercial diesel-electrics, a series of 300-hp (later 600-hp) boxcab switchers. Alco dropped out of the group in 1928, focusing on its own switcher design and buying engine builder McIntosh & Seymour in 1929.

Baldwin — the world's largest steam locomotive builder — also decided to enter the diesel-electric field, having built several earlier successful heavy electric

THE BALDWIN LOCOMOTIVE WORKS

58501   58501

Baldwin's first diesel-electric was this six-axle (A1A-A1A) boxcab with a 1,000-hp Knudsen diesel engine and Westinghouse electrical gear. After testing in 1925, it served as Baldwin's plant switcher until the early 1940s.
Trains collection

locomotives in partnership with electrical supplier Westinghouse. Carl Knudsen had developed a design for a 1,000-hp V-style, 12-cylinder diesel engine while working at Baldwin (and marketed as Knudsen Motor Corp.). Baldwin used the engine on a six-axle (A1A-A1A) boxcab locomotive with Westinghouse electrical components. It tested in 1925 on the Reading, but the results were unsatisfactory. The locomotive did, however, serve as a switcher at Baldwin's plant in Eddystone, Pa., until 1941. Baldwin would continue experiments, but with a new engine supplier: Baldwin purchased the De La Vergne Engine Co. in 1931.

Another notable landmark came in 1929, when the Canadian Locomotive Co. built a pair of boxcab passenger diesels (see page 118 in Chapter 6). Each was powered by a 1,330-hp diesel engine built by Beardmore, of Glasgow, Scotland. The bodies were designed by Baldwin, with steam-style running gear (unpowered leading and trailing trucks, with two pairs of driving axles in a heavy frame in the middle), with electrical gear from Canadian Westinghouse. Reliability was lower and expenses higher than hoped, but the locomotives were

Diesel vs. Steam, 1930-1960

Locomotives in service, Class I railroads		
	Diesel	*Steam*
1930	74	55,875
1935	113	45,614
1940	797	40,041
1945	3,816	38,853
1950	14,047	25,640
1955	24,786	5,982
1960	28,278	261

successful enough to operate through the 1930s although the design was not repeated.

These early railcars and locomotives all helped show the viability and potential of diesel-electrics for road service as well as switching, although continued improvement in reliability and efficiency were needed.

End-cab switchers

The first truly successful commercial mass-produced diesel-electrics were switching locomotives. The traditional boxcab design, taken from electric loco-

motives (and required early on because of the size of the various components) was ill-suited to switching. Even with cabs at each end, crews struggled with visibility. The solution was narrowing the body.

General Electric in 1931 built seven custom 300-hp, 60-ton switchers for Bush Terminal Railroad in Brooklyn. They were the first to feature a narrow hood with walkways (running boards) along it, with a full-width cab (in fact, they had a small nose on the other end of the cab). Although GE did not go on to build heavier switchers, the design foreshadowed the later light-duty 44- and 70-ton locomotives that GE would sell from the 1940s into the 1950s.

Alco's first switcher in its HH ("high-hood") line, a demonstrator in 1931, was the first standard, off-the-shelf end-cab switcher. The 600-hp locomotive, powered by a McIntosh & Seymour in-line six-cylinder engine, was followed by more than 170 production 600-, 660-, and 900-hp switchers (to 20 railroads) through the decade.

Other manufacturers soon followed. Electro-Motive turned out its first end-cab switcher in 1935, the 600-hp SC (actually assembled at GE, since EMC's plant was

still under construction) powered by a Winton 201A diesel engine. It was followed by more than 100 additional 600- and 900-hp Winton-engined locomotives over the next 3 years.

Baldwin built a demonstrator in 1937 and in 1939 began building 660- and 1,000-hp versions of its VO switchers. The locomotives were powered by six- and eight-cylinder versions of the VO engine developed with Baldwin's purchase of De La Vergne.

Streamliners and road freight diesels

While diesel switchers operated in relative obscurity, the Chicago, Burlington & Quincy and Union Pacific made news with new lightweight, articulated passenger trains powered by internal-combustion engines. The Burlington worked with Budd on the fluted stainless-steel *Zephyr*, while UP contracted Pullman-Standard to design the smooth-sided aluminum M-10000. Both worked with EMC (which, with Winton Engine Co., had been acquired by General Motors in 1930) to power their trains. Both trains debuted in 1934; the UP's M-10000 was first, powered by a Winton 191A

Alco's HH series was the first mass-produced end-cab switcher. Delaware, Lackawanna & Western No. 405 is a 600-hp HH600 built in 1934. The high hood was necessitated by the tall in-line model 531 diesel engine.

Trains collection

distillate engine, followed by the *Zephyr*, powered by a Winton 201A diesel.

The next several years saw additional streamliners for those and other railroads, each powered by successively more-powerful diesel engines. The power cars were initially articulated to their trains but later were built as separate units, though still styled to match specific trains.

Experiments by EMC with a double-engine, boxcab-style, stand-alone passenger diesel culminated in the first of the company's E unit streamlined locomotives in 1937, the EA, E1, and E2. These led to a line of standardized passenger locomotives built into the 1960s. Alco followed with its twin-engine DL passenger locomotives in 1939 and single-engine PA in 1946. Other less-successful streamlined designs were later built by Baldwin and Fairbanks-Morse.

The game-changer was EMC's FT freight diesel, which hit the rails as a demonstrator in 1939 with the first production models entering revenue service in 1941. Although production was slowed by World War II,

more than 1,000 were built by 1945, and its success effectively marked the end of the steam locomotive. Even though the FT's price tag was about double that of a comparative steam locomotive, the FT showed that not only could diesels handle heavy freight trains, they could do it more efficiently, saving millions in maintenance and infrastructure, including coaling towers and water tanks plus roundhouses and repair facilities.

The FT inspired a line of successively more powerful and improved streamlined freight F units from Electro-Motive (as of 1941 EMD, the Electro-Motive Division of GM), along with cab-style freight locomotives from Alco (FA, 1946), Baldwin (DR4-4-1500, 1947), and Fairbanks-Morse (C-Line, 1950).

Alco's 1,000-hp RS1 of 1941 was notable as the first road switcher. It was a stretched version of Alco's S1 switcher, placed on a longer frame with road trucks and a nose on the opposite end of the cab. It was, however, a light-duty locomotive intended for local

LOCOMOTIVE "GENERATIONS"

D iesel locomotive production has continually evolved since the 1920s, but locomotives are often classified into "generations" based on the period built. We are currently in the fourth generation of diesel-electric locomotives; here is a rough guide of their generational definitions:

First generation — These are the diesels that replaced steam locomotives directly; they include the earliest diesels through those built through the 1950s.

Second generation — These are the first diesels that were built to replace other diesels. They featured higher horsepower and larger, better engines. The start is generally marked by the introduction of GE's U25B and EMD's turbocharged GP20 and SD24 in 1959-1960, and runs until the early 1980s.

Third generation — Generally defined as the start of microprocessor control for locomotives, beginning with EMD's GP60/SD60 (1984) and GE's Dash 8 series (1985). This generation continued through the remainder of DC-traction-motor production in the early 2000s.

Fourth generation — Most consider the start of this generation to be the coming of AC traction motors, with GE and EMD both beginning production of standard models in 1993. The break between generations is a bit fuzzy, since AC and DC locomotives were built concurrently into the 2000s.

and branchline service. Baldwin in 1946 copied the idea but in a more-powerful version with its line of 1,500-hp four- and six-axle diesels, just ahead of Alco's 1,500-hp RS2 and the Fairbanks-Morse 1,500-hp H15-44 in 1947. The road switcher effectively became the standard road freight locomotive design with EMD's release of the GP7 in 1949.

Continued evolution

The chart on page 16 shows how quickly the diesel revolution took place. The numbers also show that, when dieselization was complete, it only took 28,000 diesels (in 1960) to replace the 40,000 steam locomotives in service in 1940. Diesel-electrics had not only proven to be more efficient, but their higher availability rate meant it took fewer diesels than steam locomotives to perform even more work. When you add the flexibility

of being able to assemble diesels into consists that match the needs of any given train, the advantage is apparent.

Since that period, diesel-electric locomotives have evolved significantly. They are more powerful — a standard locomotive today is 4,400 hp instead of 1,500 hp — and they are equipped with improved engine and electrical systems including advanced microprocessor monitoring and controls.

As horsepower continued to increase through the 1950s and into the 1960s, railroads opted mainly for four-axle road switchers for freight. Although EMD's six-axle SD7 and SD9 generated decent sales, they represented less than 10% of the company's road-switcher sales through the 1950s. Alco fared just a bit better with its six-axle RSD line, at 13% of Alco's road switcher sales during that time.

Electro-Motive's first end-cab diesel switchers were the 600-hp SC and SW of 1935, assembled at GE because the EMC assembly plant was still under construction. *Electro-Motive*

The era of custom power cars was in full swing in 1936 when EMC/Budd built Chicago, Burlington & Quincy's *Denver Zephyr* power units *Silver King* and *Silver Queen* (No. 9906A, B). The 1,800-hp A unit had two 12-cylinder Winton 201A engines; the 1,200-hp B unit had a single 16-cylinder Winton. *Chicago, Burlington & Quincy*

DIESEL-HYDRAULIC LOCOMOTIVES

The 1960s saw an attempt to eliminate the electrical drive on locomotives, replacing it with a mechanical/hydraulic drive connection. In 1961 Southern Pacific purchased three 3,540-hp German Kraus-Maffei diesel-hydraulic locomotives, each powered by a pair of Maybach V16 engines. These were followed by 18 additional locomotives (including three for Rio Grande, which SP later acquired), plus three twin-engine diesel-hydraulics from Alco, model Century 643DH. All used hydraulic-mechanical transmission made by the German company Voith to transfer motion from the engine driveshaft to the axles.

Although moderately successful in service, the locomotives never advanced beyond experimental status. Uneven performance on mountain grades, higher-than-standard maintenance, the specialized nature of parts, and the coming of conventional single-engine diesel-electrics of 3,000- to 3,600-hp doomed the diesel-hydraulics to early retirements, and all were off the SP roster by 1968.

The German Kraus-Maffei ML-4000 was a six-axle, 3,450-hp, twin-engine diesel-hydraulic design. The hydraulic-mechanical transmissions, which replaced the generator/traction motor drive, resembled truck differentials.
Locomotive: Louis A. Marre collection, Jr; Transmission: Kraus-Maffei

Electro-Motive's FT, more than any other diesel-electric, ensured the demise of the steam locomotive. The four-unit, 5,400-hp demonstrator (1,350 hp for each unit), built in 1939, works on the Rio Grande during its cross-country demonstration tour. *R.V. Nixon*

By the early 1960s, as railroads were boldly advertising their hotshot piggyback trains and high-speed freight services — which were assigned the newest high-horsepower four-axle diesels — some in the industry thought the six-motor freight diesel was all but dead. The notable 2,400 hp of early six-axle, high-horsepower diesels (Fairbanks-Morse's H24-66 of 1953 and Alco's RSD15 of 1955) did not generate significant sales. Railroads looked at six-axle freight locomotives as suitable only for slow-speed drag service or for local service on lightweight rail, and didn't find the extra expense (and two additional traction motors to maintain) of six-axle units worth it for general service.

This changed radically in the mid-1960s with EMD's introduction of the 3,000-hp SD40 and 3,600-hp SD45 (and later SD40-2 and SD45-2). They, along with GE's U30C (3,000 hp), U33C (3,300 hp), and U36C (3,600 hp) gave the railroads powerful locomotives that worked well not only in heavy-haul and drag service (such as coal unit trains), but for longer, heavier fast priority trains as well.

As an example, at EMD, the '40- and '45-series six-axle diesels outsold the four-axle GP40/GP40-2 at a better than 3:1 clip. In fact, it was the low-horsepower (2,000-hp) GP38/GP38-2 that became the dominant four-axle locomotive: with 2,947 built, they outsold the 3,000-hp four-axle series by almost 600 engines. Four-axle sales continued fading by the late 1980s, with the last four-axle freight

Alco gets credit for producing the first road-switcher with its 1,000-hp RS1 in 1941. The light-duty locomotive is basically an S1 switcher on a lengthened frame with road trucks and a short added nose. Great Northern No. 183 was built in 1944. *Alco*

The four-axle road switcher had become the standard road-freight locomotive by the early 1960s. Two 2,000-hp EMD GP20s, built in 1961, lead a westbound Chicago, Burlington & Quincy train west of Chicago in November 1964.
J. David Ingles

GENSET LOCOMOTIVES

Genset diesel-electric locomotives, which first appeared in 2005, were an attempt to create a locomotive that would produce lower emissions and have higher fuel efficiency compared to a standard locomotive. These locomotives have multiple engine/generator sets (two, three, or four). Each starts and stops automatically, adjusting to the load so that only as many run at one time as needed. They were built by MPI, National Railway Engineering, and RailPower Technologies, and versions were purchased by most major railroads.

Efficiencies were not as good as hoped, the locomotives required more maintenance than expected, and power and acceleration were also found lacking. None have been built for North American railroads since about 2010, and major railroads have been retiring them or selling them to short lines. Experiments are continuing with battery-electric locomotives.

This BNSF genset is an NRE-built model 3GS21B. It has three gensets, each with a Cummins QSK19 700-hp diesel engine, for 2,100 total hp.
David Lustig

The EMD SD40 began the shift to six-axle road locomotives for most applications. Gulf, Mobile & Ohio No. 950 leads two sisters on a freight in 1970; the 950 is the first SD40, built as EMD demonstrator No. 434 in July 1964. *J. David Ingles*

diesel built in 1994 (GP60s for St. Louis Southwestern).

The most radical change in diesel-electric development has been the shift to AC traction motors, which provide significant advantages over DC motors for adhesion, reliability, resistance to overheating, and dynamic brake control. Modern locomotives also comply with the EPA's strict Tier-4 emissions regulations.

As of 2020, there were just over 38,000 locomotives in service in North America, down slightly from a high of 39,500 in 2017. Regardless of their builder and features, all trace their roots back to those pioneering early diesels of the 1920s and 1930s.

Turn the page and we'll begin looking at how a diesel locomotive works, starting first with the engine and related systems, then moving through the electrical systems, trucks, body design, braking systems, and ancillary devices and details.

The adaptation of microprocessor control and AC traction motors marks the latest (fourth) generation of diesel-electric locomotives. A 4,400-hp EMD SD70ACe demonstrator poses in March 2013. *Jim Wrinn*

CHAPTER 2

HOW DIESEL ENGINES WORK

Starting with fuel and ending with power, here is what happens inside an engine when it is operating

The diesel engine itself is the heart of any locomotive. Engines — also known as "prime movers" — have not only grown larger since the first diesel locomotives, they have become more powerful, smaller in size for their power output, and have increased in efficiency and reliability. They are also much more ecologically friendly, with new locomotives subject to strict limits on emissions.

In this chapter we'll look at the engine itself and its many components. We'll start with the basics of how a diesel engine works, then examine the individual components and systems including fuel, lubricating oil, air supply, and the radiator and water-cooling. Chapter 3 will examine several particular engine designs from multiple builders.

Each locomotive builder developed its own diesel engine designs. Some were short-

A worker checks out the model 710 engine through the hood doors of an EMD SD70ACe demonstrator locomotive in 2012. The modern two-cycle, V16 diesel traces its roots back to Electro-Motive's innovative model 567 engine of the late 1930s. *Jim Wrinn*

lived and problematic, but others remained in production for decades. Regardless of the specific design, many functions and components were common across all engines. And within any given engine series, parts are interchangeable — a great appeal to railroads. In other words, the same spare exhaust valve would fit any version of an EMD 567-series engine, whether an eight-cylinder switcher, a 12-cylinder passenger engine, or a 16-cylinder freight engine.

As Chapter 1 noted, early diesel engines were large, heavy, and slow. Applying a diesel to a locomotive was an entirely different proposition compared to a ship or stationary power plant. Unlike those environments, a locomotive's interior provides a limited amount of space. A locomotive engine is also subject to constant rocking and jarring motion from rough track, plus impact forces from coupling and slack running in and out. It also must operate in all types of weather and conditions, from below-zero cold to triple-digit desert heat, and run at high altitudes where air is thin.

A locomotive engine is also largely untended while running. Unlike a stationary or ship engine that receives constant attention, a locomotive engine is largely ignored from terminal to terminal unless a problem occurs that limits its power or shuts it down.

Basic diesel engine design

The basic principle of how a diesel engine works is easy to understand. Its core is the engine block (also called cylinder block or crankcase), a heavy cast iron or fabricated steel (weldment) structure that is then machined. A series of cylinders bored into the engine block each hold a piston. Each piston is connected by a rod to the crankshaft, which runs the length of the engine. The cylinders can be vertical and all arranged in a straight line ("in-line" or "straight" engine) or in pairs at an angle ("V" engine).

Burning a fuel/air mix at the top of the cylinders — each carefully timed in order — propels the pistons downward. The fuel and air admission is provided by a series of valves, with motion regulated by a camshaft. The movement of the pistons, via the connecting rods, turns the crankshaft. On a diesel-electric locomotive, the crankshaft motion turns a generator or alternator (as opposed to a

A new Chesapeake & Ohio F7 under construction at EMD in 1952 has a 16-cylinder 567 engine installed on the frame, with a D12 generator at left. At far left, a worker installs components in the electrical cabinet that will serve as the wall between the cab and engine room. *EMD*

direct-drive transmission, as on trucks, autos, and many other vehicles). The resulting electricity goes to traction motors which in turn power the locomotive's axles and wheels. Chapter 4 explains these electrical systems.

Unlike a gasoline or distillate engine that requires a separate spark (from a spark plug) to ignite the fuel, a diesel has no separate spark source. Instead, the diesel relies on compression heat for ignition. Compressing air creates heat, and a piston on its upstroke compresses the intake air to a pressure up to 500 pounds per square inch, generating a temperature of about 1,000 F. An atomized spray of diesel fuel is then injected into the cylinder and burns; the resulting pressure from the expanding gases sends the piston downward.

Upward piston motion expels exhaust gases out from the top of the cylinder through valves to a manifold (on normally aspirated/non-turbocharged engines) and then upward out of exhaust stacks — generally two to four depending upon the amount of back pressure generated. On turbocharged

engines, the exhaust passes through the turbo (more on those in a moment) and then out a single stack. On these locomotives, the turbocharger acts as a spark arrestor, while non-turbo engines sometimes have separate spark arrestors on the stacks to keep any stray burning embers from escaping.

The high pressure, heat, and forces involved require diesel engines to have heavy components, which means that diesel engines are robust, strong, and long-lasting compared to gasoline engines. The heat involved, and the changes in temperature (for example, a piston head repeatedly being exposed to the firing of fuel, then hit with incoming cool combustion air), can lead to stresses, metal fatigue, and cracking or component failure. A large part of diesel evolutionary design has involved metallurgy, coming up with the best materials for each component.

Locomotive engines need to be large enough to provide sufficient power for their use, which varies by locomotive type. Most engines are built in multiple sizes with identical cylinder sizes and components, but

Diesel locomotives allowed railroads to easily store common parts. Santa Fe's Argentine (Kan.) Shops in 1954 show (clockwise from left) new and refurbished EMD valves, pistons, connecting rod (on hoist), and cylinder liners.
Santa Fe

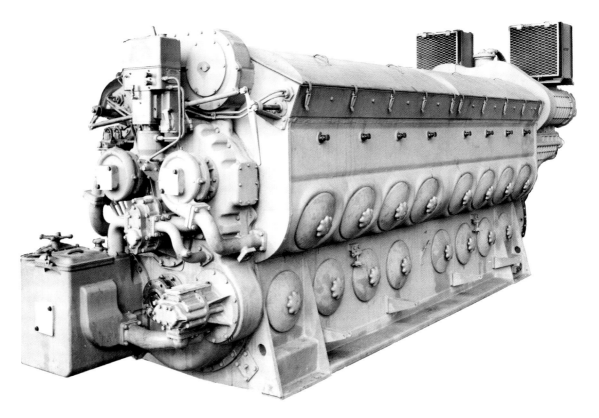

Electro-Motive's 567 engine was one of the most-successful engines of all time, with versions used from the late 1930s to mid-1960s. This 16-cylinder, V-style 567C engine, built in November 1953, is bound for a new GP9 or F9. *EMD*

with additional banks of cylinders to provide more power as needed. For example, EMD's 567 engine was built in 6-, 8-, 12-, and 16-cylinder variants to power small and large switchers, twin-engine passenger locomotives, and various types of road freight locomotives.

Engines are heavy: about 18 tons for a 16-cylinder version of EMD's 645 engine, plus another 2,300 pounds for the turbocharger; a new 12-cylinder Wabtec GEVO engine weighs about 22 tons.

Engine speed (measured by crankshaft rpm) varies by design. Many in-line engines with larger cylinders/pistons will have slower top speeds (about 600-700 rpm) than V-style engines. V-style engines typically have a top speed around 900 to 950 rpm. High-speed engines have also been used. Example: the Cummins QSK95 in the 4,000-hp Siemens Charger passenger locomotives, which have a top speed of 1,200 rpm.

Engine speed and fuel use rate are controlled by the governor, which determines how much fuel is injected for each cycle of the piston. Each throttle setting has a set rate for engine speed; the governor must keep

the engine at that speed, regardless of the load imposed by the generator/alternator. Engine overspeed can damage or destroy the generator and/or the engine. The governor's mechanical connection to the fuel injectors, and the injectors themselves, are called the "fuel rack." The engine's fuel rack position is controlled by the governor, which determines how much fuel is needed to maintain the desired engine (rpm) speed. These settings can be altered to suit the engine.

Among the biggest changes in diesel engine evolution has been the addition of computer microprocessors to monitor and control functions. Engines into the 1980s required mechanical controls and sensors to regulate temperature, speed, fuel injection, and other tasks. Since then, microprocessors have become more prevalent. Today's Tier 4-compliant engines, such as EMD's 1010J and Wabtec's GEVO, have extensive computer controls that are essential for managing cooling (water and air) systems, which are critical to lowering emissions. Additional microprocessors monitor performance, control traction and wheel slip,

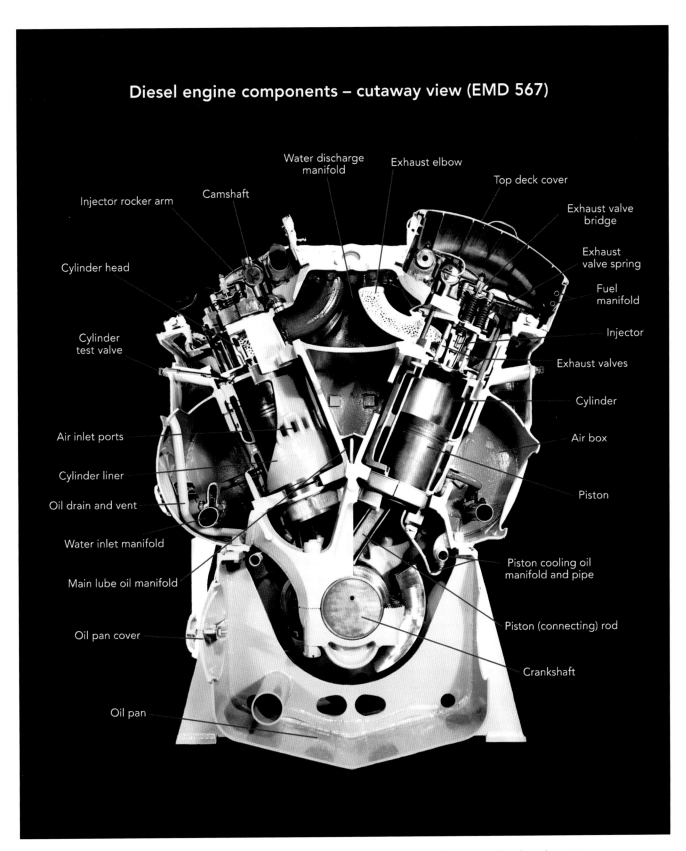

Diesel engine components – cutaway view (EMD 567)

Water discharge manifold

Exhaust elbow

Top deck cover

Injector rocker arm

Camshaft

Exhaust valve bridge

Exhaust valve spring

Cylinder head

Fuel manifold

Injector

Cylinder test valve

Exhaust valves

Cylinder

Air inlet ports

Air box

Cylinder liner

Piston

Oil drain and vent

Water inlet manifold

Piston cooling oil manifold and pipe

Main lube oil manifold

Oil pan cover

Piston (connecting) rod

Crankshaft

Oil pan

This cross-section view of an EMD 567 engine highlights the major components of a V-style diesel engine. *EMD*

and track and store data that can identify and diagnose problems and potential problems with almost any on-board system, including engine, fuel, oil, cooling, brake, control, and electrical.

Opposed-piston engines

Special mention is needed for the Fairbanks-Morse opposed-piston (OP) engine, a marine design produced by FM that it adopted for its line of diesel locomotives introduced toward the end of World War II.

In-line (straight) engines have all cylinders placed vertically in a line. This is a turbocharged eight-cylinder, 1,600-hp Baldwin 608A engine. It's coupled to a Westinghouse generator at left; the auxiliary generator is mounted atop the main generator, with the drive belt enclosed in a cage. *Baldwin*

DISTILLATE ENGINES

The distillate engine was a cross between a gasoline engine and a diesel engine.

As early railcars with gas engines were requiring more power, they became larger. However, the economies of a gasoline engine fall off with size, and above 300 hp, a cheaper-fuel, more-efficient design was needed — at least until a diesel engine of compact size could be developed.

Into the early 1930s Winton (under the lead of Dick Dilworth, chief engineer for Electro-Motive) developed designs for a high-horsepower distillate engine. Distillate was comprised of a variety of fuels ranging from kerosene to naptha to gas oil — basically liquid products that were, in the 1920s, left over from a refinery's cracking process.

Distillate at the time was primarily used in small engines in tractors and other agricultural equipment (and was sometimes called "tractor fuel"). Its greatest advantage was that it was cheap: about 3 cents a gallon in the mid-1920s, compared to 15 cents for gasoline.

The eventual result was Winton's 900-hp model 194 engine (used by EMC only in Santa Fe's M-190 articulated motor car) and 191A engine, a V-style 12-cylinder design rated at 600 hp used most notably in Union Pacific's M-10000 — the first internal-combustion streamliner.

Large distillate engines suffered from many challenges and problems.

Since distillate was difficult to ignite, each cylinder required four spark plugs, all operating at significantly higher voltage than those on a gasoline engine. It also required a heavy carburetor on each cylinder pair. The heavy fuel tended to foul the plugs quickly. This made the engines maintenance intensive, even when they were working properly.

Dilworth described engine use of distillate as "trying to set fire to a wet haystack."

As development of the Winton 201A diesel progressed, it quickly became the focus of EMC/Winton, and the distillate engines were discontinued.

Inline engine cross-section
(Baldwin 600 series SC)

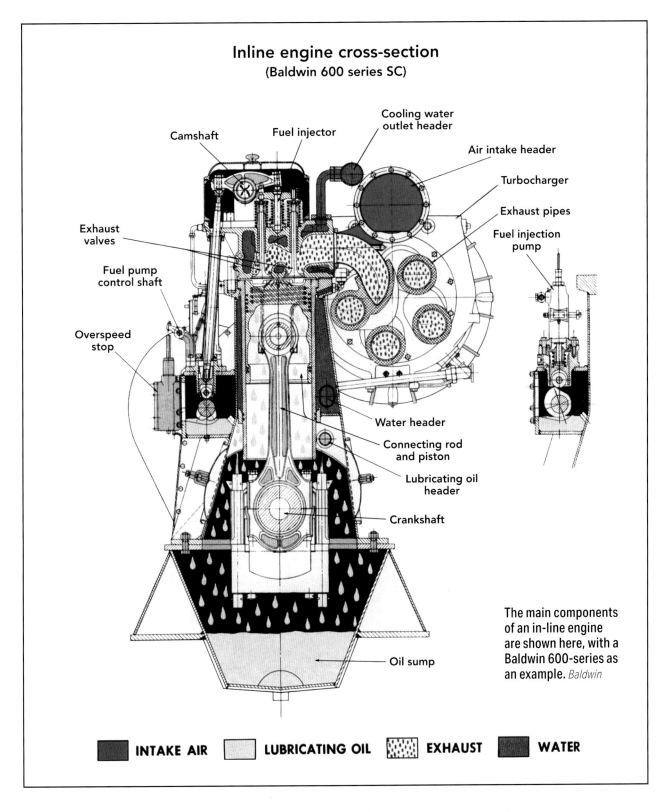

Camshaft

Fuel injector

Cooling water outlet header

Air intake header

Turbocharger

Exhaust pipes

Fuel injection pump

Exhaust valves

Fuel pump control shaft

Overspeed stop

Water header

Connecting rod and piston

Lubricating oil header

Crankshaft

Oil sump

The main components of an in-line engine are shown here, with a Baldwin 600-series as an example. *Baldwin*

■ **INTAKE AIR**   ▨ **LUBRICATING OIL**   ▨ **EXHAUST**   ■ **WATER**

The OP is a tall, in-line design with two pistons in each cylinder. There's no cylinder head — instead, the top piston drives an upper crankshaft. A vertical shaft at one end of the engine block connects the upper and lower crankshafts, combining the power.

The benefits of an OP engine are increased power for a given engine size and no cylinder heads or head gaskets to maintain. Disadvantages were increased air and cooling requirements, and the challenge of having to remove the upper crankshaft to do major

31

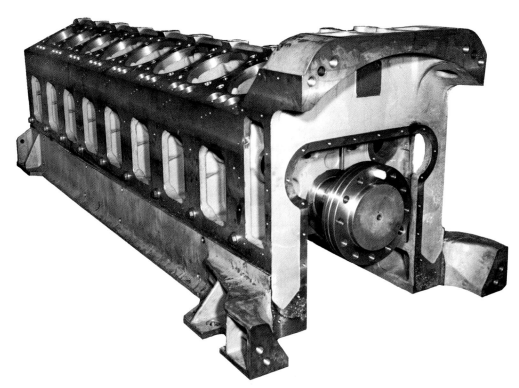

The engine block is the core of the engine. This is a cast and machined block for a General Electric 7FDL16 engine, destined for use in a U25B locomotive in the early 1960s.

General Electric

EMD 265H engine

This three-dimensional view shows the major components of a modern diesel engine, in this case a four-cycle, 16-cylinder, twin-turbocharger EMD 265H.

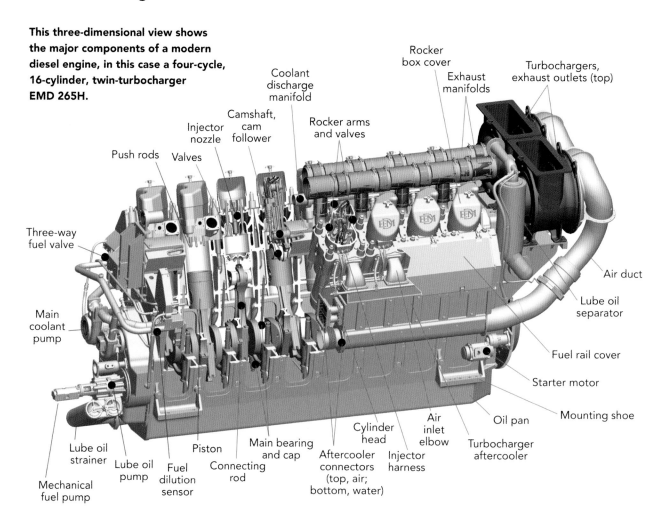

maintenance to the engine. Although OP engines worked well in submarines, ships, and power plants where they received constant care and maintenance, they weren't as successful on locomotives. See page 65 in Chapter 3 for more details on OP design.

Four- and two-cycle engines

Diesel engines fall into two basic designs: four- or two-cycle. A four-cycle engine requires four piston strokes (two up, two down, with two revolutions of the crankshaft) to accomplish one power stroke. A two-cycle

engine requires two strokes (one up, one down, one revolution of the crankshaft) to get one power stroke. Here's how they differ (*see the diagrams on page 34 and 35*):

Four-cycle: The process starts with the intake stroke, where the piston descends and clean air is drawn into the cylinder through the air inlet ports. The piston then moves upward, sealing off the inlet ports and compressing the air as it reaches its highest position. Fuel is atomized and admitted by the fuel injector; the air/fuel mix burns, propelling the piston downward on its power

The Fairbanks-Morse Model 38 engine is an opposed-piston design, with two pistons in each vertical cylinder. *Fairbanks-Morse*

Fairbanks-Morse opposed-piston engine
Side cutaway view

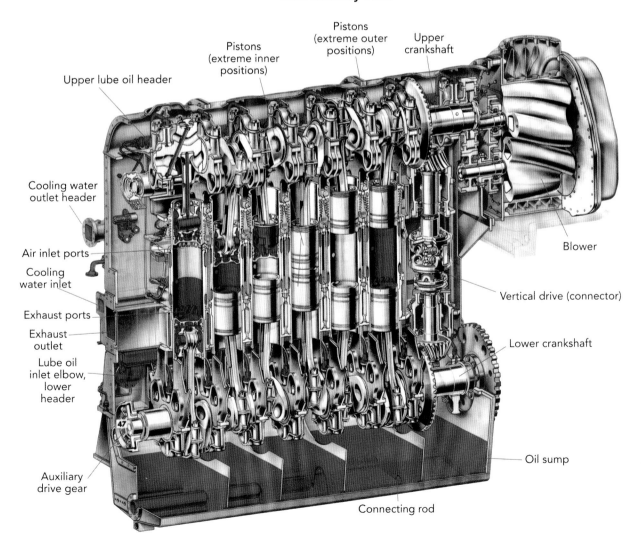

Pistons (extreme inner positions)

Pistons (extreme outer positions)

Upper crankshaft

Upper lube oil header

Cooling water outlet header

Air inlet ports

Cooling water inlet

Exhaust ports

Exhaust outlet

Lube oil inlet elbow, lower header

Auxiliary drive gear

Blower

Vertical drive (connector)

Lower crankshaft

Oil sump

Connecting rod

This view of an Electro-Motive FT without roof panels shows how the exhaust elbows lead upward to the exhaust manifold (muffler) above the engine, with four exhaust stacks. It also illustrates how cramped the working space was inside a car-body locomotive. *EMC*

FOUR-CYCLE DIESEL

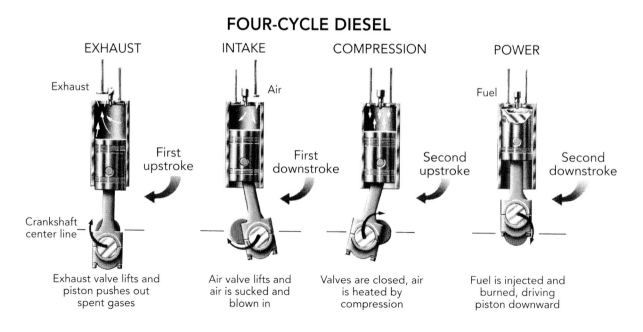

EXHAUST	INTAKE	COMPRESSION	POWER
Exhaust	Air		Fuel
First upstroke	First downstroke	Second upstroke	Second downstroke
Crankshaft center line			
Exhaust valve lifts and piston pushes out spent gases	Air valve lifts and air is sucked and blown in	Valves are closed, air is heated by compression	Fuel is injected and burned, driving piston downward

stroke. As the piston rises back upward, it forces the spent gases out of the exhaust valves at the top of the cylinder to the exhaust elbow. The process is then repeated.

Two-cycle: As the piston goes downward, the cylinder admits clean combustion air; this combustion air simultaneously forces spent gases out the exhaust valves. As the piston travels upward, the air inlets are closed off, the exhaust valves close, the piston compresses the clean air, and fuel is injected, which burns and forces the piston down, repeating the cycle. Because this all must happen in two piston strokes, the process is much faster than a four-cycle engine (this all happens in about 1/50th of a second for an engine turning at 900 rpm). More air is required because of the need for the incoming combustion air to also force out the spent gases.

With either type of engine, the pistons/ cylinders work in unison in a regulated order of firing. Thus while one piston is at the top of its cylinder, others will be at various points in their motion. This applies even motion and consistent force and power to the crankshaft.

Electro-Motive relied on two-cycle engines until the 1990s, while other builders primarily used four-cycle designs, with all modern locomotives powered by four-cycle designs. Which design was best? That's up to railroads and engineers to figure out. Four-cycle designs tend to be more fuel efficient, but were more complex; two-cycle designs historically burned more fuel but were easier to maintain because of component locations and requirements.

Let's take a closer look at key engine components.

Cylinders, pistons, and injectors

The cylinders are bored into the engine block. The common methods of stating the engine size are by the number of cylinders, the cubic-inch volume of each cylinder, the total volume of the engine, and by the bore diameter and piston stroke distance (EMD's 567 engine, for example, had a volume of 567 cubic inches per cylinder, with an 8½ x 10-inch bore/stroke. The variance in cylinder size is why the number of cylinders by itself isn't an accurate measure of power — a modern 12-cylinder EMD 1010J engine is more powerful than an older 16-cylinder 567 or 645 engine.

TWO-CYCLE DIESEL

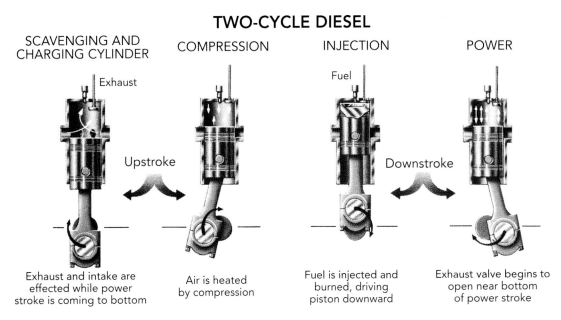

SCAVENGING AND CHARGING CYLINDER — Exhaust — Upstroke — Exhaust and intake are effected while power stroke is coming to bottom

COMPRESSION — Air is heated by compression

INJECTION — Fuel — Downstroke — Fuel is injected and burned, driving piston downward

POWER — Exhaust valve begins to open near bottom of power stroke

Kalmbach Media

Piston/connecting rod assembly
(EMD 567B)

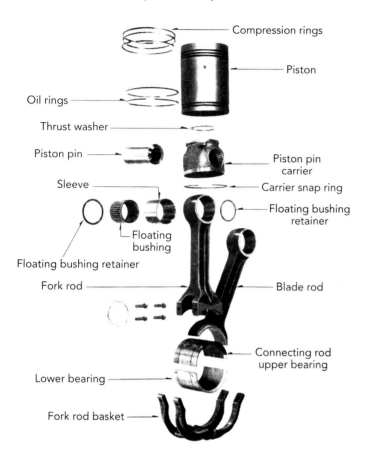

Compression rings
Piston
Oil rings
Thrust washer
Piston pin
Piston pin carrier
Sleeve
Carrier snap ring
Floating bushing retainer
Floating bushing
Floating bushing retainer
Fork rod
Blade rod
Connecting rod upper bearing
Lower bearing
Fork rod basket

Fuel injector

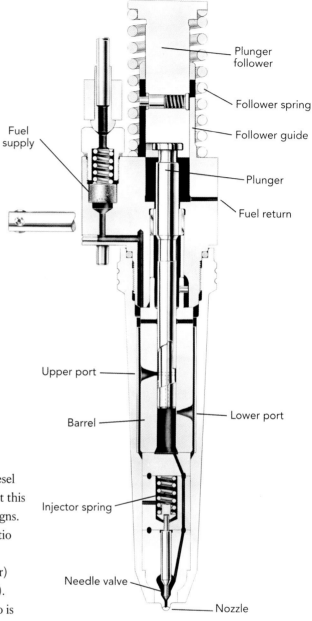

Plunger follower
Follower spring
Follower guide
Fuel supply
Plunger
Fuel return
Upper port
Lower port
Barrel
Injector spring
Needle valve
Nozzle

Above: The piston attaches to the crankshaft via the connecting rod. The blade rod nests in the fork rod, allowing the paired pistons in a V-style engine to work together at a single connection point on the driveshaft. This is the design from an EMD 567 engine. *EMD*

Above right: The injector pushes fuel into the cylinder just before the piston reaches top dead center. The needle valve is designed to atomize fuel to a fine spray ensuring complete combustion. This is an EMD design first used in 1959. *EMD*

A typical compression ratio for a diesel locomotive engine is about 15-to-1, but this varies among builders and specific designs. An engine's compression ratio is the ratio between the volume in the cylinder at its largest (piston at bottom dead center) and smallest (piston at top dead center). Compared to gasoline engines, the ratio is higher for diesels because of the pressure required for ignition.

Each cylinder has a cast-iron liner that is plated or hardened to enable the piston to slide smoothly within it. Having a separate liner means the inevitable friction wear is on the liner and not the engine block itself. Cylinder liners can be replaced or restored as needed, or when an engine is rebuilt or reconditioned. Cylinder heads serve as the top of the combustion chamber, and are also cast iron. The heads are subject to extreme temperature changes and pressure stress, and

are water-cooled via cored passages. The cylinder head fits atop the engine block, with a tight seal needed at the joint, which is provided by the head gasket.

Pistons are made from cast iron, aluminum alloy, or aluminum plated with a steel cap. They have a series of grooves around their circumference at the top and bottom that hold piston rings, which provide the contact surfaces with the cylinder liner. The rings at top (compression rings) keep combustion air from leaking downward; the rings at the

bottom (oil rings) keep lubrication oil from leaking upward to the combustion chamber. The rings are designed to take the brunt of wear from the piston itself.

The rings require periodic replacing. Their wear can lead to a loss of compression (and thus power) and can allow oil leaks; more severe damage or failure can lead to a piston cracking or failing, which can damage the engine or crankshaft.

Steel connecting rods, as their name implies, connect the bottom of the piston to the crankshaft. They convert the up-and-down motion of the pistons to circular motion at the crankshaft. The piston/cylinder/connecting rod — the main components of the "power assembly" — operate at high speed and high temperature. All parts require tight tolerances (to a few thousandths of an inch) to work properly, and cooling and lubrication are

critical. Most have grooves or internal passages that allow the movement of oil for lubrication and cooling (more on those systems in a bit).

The fuel injector is at the top of the cylinder, and its job is atomizing and spraying a precisely measured amount of diesel fuel into the cylinder at the proper moment when air has been compressed — just before the piston reaches top dead center. Because of the high pressure of compression, fuel must be forced in at even greater pressure (3,000 pounds per square inch and higher). This pressure comes from a fuel-injection pump (plunger) or unit injector. The coming of microprocessor control has led to electronic fuel injection in modern locomotives. The governor sets the amount of fuel (based on throttle setting), which is first admitted to the body of the injector; this fuel is then injected at the proper time.

Workers lower power assemblies into the cylinders of an EMD engine block. The assembly includes the cylinder liner, piston, connecting rod, and cylinder head (with valves and springs).
EMD

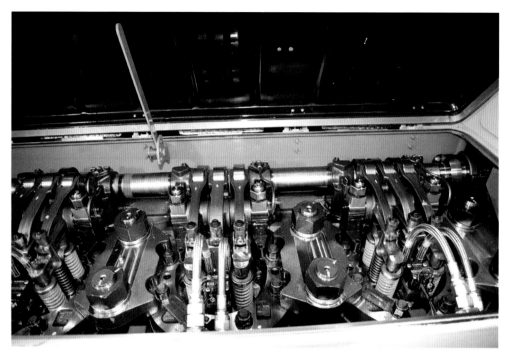

A peek inside the top of an EMD 710 engine shows the camshaft (at rear), with valves and springs as well as fuel lines leading to the injectors. *Jim Wrinn*

Locomotive crankshafts are large and heavy but must be balanced precisely. This is a crankshaft for an Alco model 251 16-cylinder engine, destined for a new locomotive in 1956. *Alco*

Crankshaft and connecting rods

The crankshaft rests on forward, rear, and intermediate bearings. Connecting rods attach at offset cranks along the shaft. *EMD*

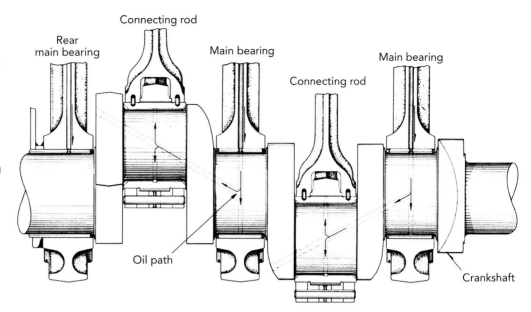

Connecting rod

Rear main bearing

Main bearing

Connecting rod

Main bearing

Oil path

Crankshaft

The timing of the fuel injectors, along with those of the exhaust valves, is critical. They are regulated by rockers triggered by rotation of the camshaft. One or more camshafts run along the length of the engine. The camshaft is connected by gears to the crankshaft to ensure proper timing.

Crankshaft

The crankshaft is considered the backbone of an engine. Crankshaft or main generator failure are the most costly repairs to a locomotive, and often trigger the retirement of older locomotives.

The crankshaft is a hardened steel shaft that travels through the lower part of the engine to a connection with the main generator. A series of offset crank throws provide connection points to the connecting rods (and thus pistons). The offset of these throws are at specific angles to each other to balance the shaft's rotational forces. Some longer shafts are two pieces joined end to end, with the mating sections flanged to align precisely and bolted together in the middle.

Despite its size, a locomotive crankshaft

Roots blower

Lobes, turning on shafts powered by the driveshaft, compress intake air and send it to the engine.
Photo: EMD; Illustration: Kalmbach Media

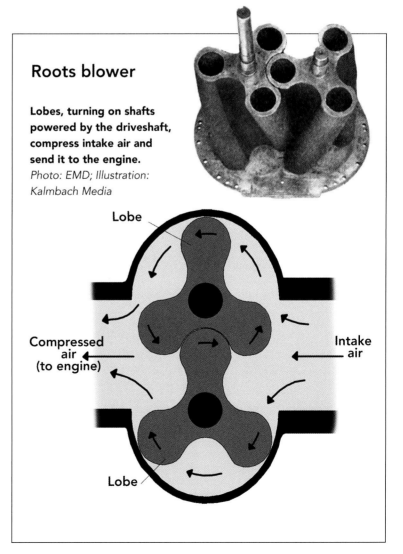

Lobe

Compressed air (to engine)

Intake air

Lobe

39

DIESEL ENGINES IN OTHER APPLICATIONS

This book focuses on engines used mainly as locomotive prime movers in North America, but it's important to understand that many of the same engines (or similar adapted designs) were and are widely used for other purposes, or were adapted from other uses (mostly naval vessels or stationary power plants). Even though a specific engine type may not have succeeded widely as a locomotive engine, it may have had great success and wide use in other applications. For example, there are still many Alco 251 and FM 38 8⅛ engines serving well as stationary power plants and in other service, decades after they largely disappeared from railroad applications (with components — and sometimes full engines —still being manufactured).

has tight tolerances and clearances along its bearings. It's essential that shaft bearings be seated properly and not worn excessively, and proper lubrication and cooling are critical. The end of the crankshaft is connected to an alternator or generator (more on those in Chapter 4) on one end, and many have a flywheel on the other end, helping to smooth and stabilize its motion.

In designing engines, the sizes and speeds of all operating parts and housings are carefully considered by engineers. Unintended sympathetic harmonic tuning among parts of similar frequency can generate excessive vibrations that can be at best annoying, and at worst, damage components.

Turbocharger (cutaway)

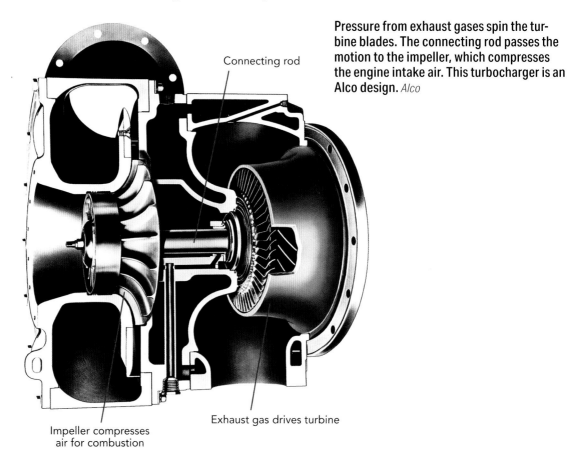

Connecting rod

Impeller compresses air for combustion

Exhaust gas drives turbine

Pressure from exhaust gases spin the turbine blades. The connecting rod passes the motion to the impeller, which compresses the engine intake air. This turbocharger is an Alco design. *Alco*

Blowers and turbochargers

To get more power out of an engine without making the engine itself larger, it has to burn more fuel. To do that requires more air; the solution is a device that forces combustion air into the engine at high pressure: a blower or turbocharger. Modern diesels are all turbocharged, but through the 1980s, manufacturers approached engine design differently, offering a mix of non-turbocharged (normally aspirated) and turbocharged engines.

Engines on diesel locomotives through the mid-1930s were normally aspirated. This changed as railroads and manufacturers began looking for higher power output. Alco in 1937 was the first to use a turbocharger, applying one to its four-cycle, eight-cylinder, 600-hp model 531 engine to create the 800-hp 531T for switchers.

Electro-Motive chose to not turbocharge its two-cycle Winton 201A and later 567 engines, instead relying on a Roots blower to boost air pressure (about 4 pounds per square inch for a Roots blower compared to 15 to 25 pounds per square inch for a turbocharger); FM did the same with its OP engine. The

Roots blower is a simple lobe-based air pump geared to the driveshaft. Its main purpose was not boosting horsepower, but providing the additional air needed to quickly scavenge spent gases from the two-cycle engine. One blower was used on small engines, with two blowers on 12-cylinder and larger engines. Turbochargers would become an option on EMD locomotives with its 567 and 645 engines starting with the GP20 and SD24 in 1959; turbos became standard for EMD with the introduction of its 710 engine in the 1980s.

For GE and most other builders, turbos were standard on road diesels, with switchers often using non-turbocharged versions.

Turbochargers work by harnessing the pressure of expelled exhaust gases to turn a turbine, which impels combustion air at high pressure into the engine. Because compressing air generates heat, most systems eventually began using an aftercooler or intercooler to lower the air temperature before it's introduced to the engine.

The turbine spins at extremely high speed — 15,000 rpm or higher. This makes turbochargers subject to high temperatures and friction, meaning that all bearing surfaces

Heavy smoke was a sign of "turbo lag" on many early diesels, primarily Alcos. When throttling up, the turbo took time to get to speed, so the combustion air didn't match the increased fuel input — the result was smoke from incomplete fuel burn. This is a Soo Line Alco RS3 in the 1960s.
J. David Ingles

41

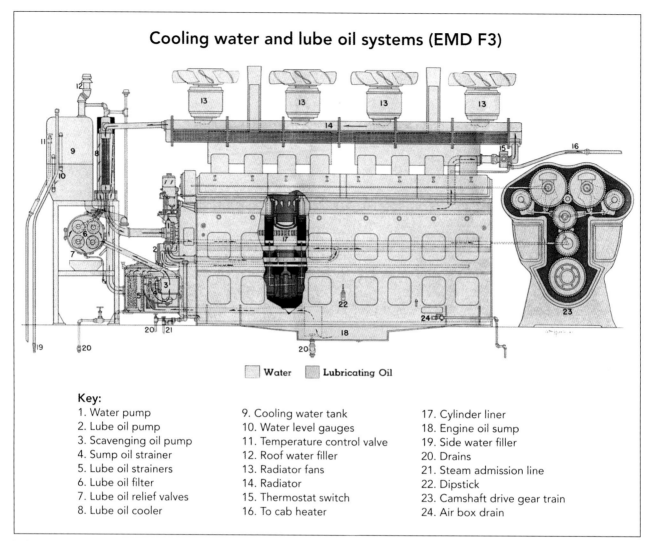

Cooling water and lube oil systems (EMD F3)

☐ Water ▨ Lubricating Oil

Key:

1. Water pump
2. Lube oil pump
3. Scavenging oil pump
4. Sump oil strainer
5. Lube oil strainers
6. Lube oil filter
7. Lube oil relief valves
8. Lube oil cooler

9. Cooling water tank
10. Water level gauges
11. Temperature control valve
12. Roof water filler
13. Radiator fans
14. Radiator
15. Thermostat switch
16. To cab heater

17. Cylinder liner
18. Engine oil sump
19. Side water filler
20. Drains
21. Steam admission line
22. Dipstick
23. Camshaft drive gear train
24. Air box drain

Lubricating oil (which also provides cooling) and engine cooling water are vital to engine operation. Both are closed systems, with piping and internal conduits routed throughout the engine and components. This is an EMD 567 engine in an F3. *EMD*

must be evenly lubricated, with external cooling a requirement. Early Alco turbos used air for cooling; chronic failures meant a switch to water-cooled turbos (with earlier turbochargers retrofitted) by the early 1950s. The high rotational speeds also mean that balance of the shaft and blades is extremely important. Even minor blade damage can lead to balance issues and turbo failure.

The Union Pacific together with AirResearch in 1955 began experimenting with turbocharging EMD 567-engined locomotives. Although a solid design, the stock 567 suffered from lower power output when operated at high altitudes (because of the thinner air). The turbos improved

the engine's performance and led to EMD introducing turbocharged versions of its SD and GP models as the SD24 (in 1958) and GP20 (1959). The SD24 had 2,400 hp compared to the 1,800 hp of the non-turbo SD18; the GP20 was 2,000 hp to the 1,800-hp non-turbo GP18.

The EMD turbocharger featured a different design than Alco's. EMD's turbo is gear driven off the driveshaft at low speeds, then clutches to exhaust driven as the engine approaches its full load at speed. This helped eliminate "turbo lag," a situation where when throttling up, increased fuel was introduced to the engine but was not burned completely because the turbo took a few seconds to get

They may be large, but diesel engines have a dipstick that must be checked periodically like an auto or truck. A worker checks the oil on a CSX (ex-Louisville & Nashville) General Electric C30-7 in 1981.

C. Norman Beasley; CSX

up to speed (marked by increased soot/smoke from the stack).

Modern diesels use multiple turbochargers, in large part to control emissions: EMD's four-cycle 1010J engine uses two-stage turbocharging (three turbochargers; one high-pressure and two low-pressure), the GE/Wabtec GEVO has two turbochargers (one high- and one low-pressure), and the Cummins QSK95 diesel in Siemens Charger passenger locomotives has four single-stage turbos. These turbos work efficiently at high and low speeds and are all microprocessor controlled for efficiency, power, and emissions control.

Lubricating oil

Lubrication of moving parts and bearing surfaces is vital to an engine's smooth operation and durability. Lube oil does several things: It provides a film on surfaces that limits friction wear between contact points and bearings; it cools components by flowing over and through them to transfer heat; and it carries away contaminants (dirt, metal particulates from component wear), which are then captured by filters.

Lube oil systems vary by manufacturer and engine design, but the basic principles are the same. The drawing on page 42 shows an example of oil and water systems as applied to an EMD 567 engine in an F unit.

Radiator (GE U25B)

Dynamic brake grids

Radiator sections

Flow control valve

Storage tank

Because of their size, locomotives require a larger quantity of oil compared to a highway-vehicle engine. Capacity has ranged from 80 gallons for an early Alco switcher (539 engine) to 165 gallons for an EMD 12-cylinder 567 engine to 250 to 350 gallons for most road diesels through the 1970s to 468 gallons for a modern Wabtec GEVO engine.

The oil is held in a pan ("sump") below the engine. A pump pulls it from the sump (via a pipe at the lowest point in the sump) and routes it upward through multiple filters and a cooler, where water from the radiator system removes heat. From there, separate piping and channels within components carry the oil to all areas of the engine, including cylinders/pistons, valves, camshaft, turbocharger bearings, and crankshaft. Oil is captured after passing through components and returned to the sump, where it begins the process again.

Oil systems operate at a pressure of 45-85 pounds per square inch (depending on builder/model), with a typical operating temperature around 195 degrees. If oil pressure drops to an unsafe level (because of a leak, low oil level, plugged filter, overheating, or

the viscosity of the oil breaking down because of contamination) or if the temperature rises excessively, sensors set off an alarm and will trigger an engine to go to idle or shut down to avoid potential damage.

Since locomotive oil — unlike oil in your automobile — isn't changed on a frequent basis, filtration is critical to keeping oil clean. Locomotive oil filters are changed on a regular basis. Today's modern oils are formulated specifically for locomotives (usually SAE 20W-40) to work with emissions equipment, and they're much more stable and resistant to breakdown compared to oil used in the early diesel era. Railroads test locomotive oil on a regular basis for particulate matter (the types of which can indicate specific issues with an engine) and a chemical analysis identifies impurities such as fuel or water and show if the oil is breaking down. Railroads may do a partial or complete oil change based on the test results.

Radiator and cooling

The water cooling system and radiator of a locomotive are responsible for controlling engine heat, ensuring that the operating

Cooling is an important part of emissions control, which is one reason modern locomotives like this GE ET44AC have such large radiator cores and sections. *Cody Grivno*

An example of modular unit construction is this fan/blower assembly for GE's U25B. The top two fans rest directly under the radiator, pulling cooling air through side screens and routing it upward through the radiator. The center housing is the axial flow equipment blower, which forces all air for equipment ventilation through an air cleaner and through channels in the frame. *General Electric*

temperature remains constant regardless of operating or atmospheric conditions. The radiator and fans dispel heat, and on modern engines radiators have become more complex, as they also play an important role in controlling emissions.

The water-cooling system is a pressurized, closed circuit with typical capacity of 225 to 350 gallons of water for locomotives into the 1980s and up to 440 gallons for modern units. Locomotives, generally, do not use antifreeze, mainly because of the risk of alcohol-based antifreeze contaminating the lube oil system in case of a leak. Some modern locomotives have

the ability to use antifreeze, but the practice is rare. Coolant water is, however, treated with anti-corrosion chemicals.

The system consists of a storage tank, a pump with piping that circulates the water throughout the engine, through the oil cooler (to regulate oil temperature), to the turbocharger, to the turbo aftercooler, then to one or more radiators. Operating temperature is about 175 degrees.

The radiator is located at roof level at the rear of the long hood on most road switchers and directly above the engine on other locomotives (notably EMD E and F units and

In the 1970s, EMD built "tunnel motor" SD40T-2 and SD45T-2 (shown) variations of its six-axle, high-horsepower road switchers. The lowered radiator intake was designed to capture cooler air while operating in snowsheds and tunnels. Southern Pacific was the main customer.
Southern Pacific

Electro-Motive locomotives have roof-mounted cooling fans. The boxy enclosure covering one radiator fan is a winterization hatch. In cold weather, it allows routing warm air back into the engine compartment.
Trains collection

other cab designs). Switchers often have a vertical radiator and fan at the end of the hood, marked by a grill or screened opening on the end.

Water is cooled in the radiator by one or more fans, with specific methods varying by builder. Fans may be visible atop the roof above the radiator (EMD), where they pull cooling air through grilles on the sides, through the radiator, and upward through the fans. Others (GE and Alco) have used fans under the radiator or roof.

Early diesels used mechanically driven fans, but electric drive was soon favored due to the complexity of routing operating belts in the engine room. On early diesels, all water flowed through the radiators; thermostatic controls turned each fan on or off and opened or closed air-intake shutters as needed to regulate water temperature.

On modern EMD engines, radiators use a

FUEL CONSUMPTION

Locomotive engines use much more fuel than a highway vehicle. The exact amount, however, varies widely based on the specific engine and locomotive, combined with its throttle setting and load. Because train speeds and loads vary — for example, a 60-mph piggyback hotshot rolling across level prairie vs. a heavy coal train climbing a mountain grade at 10 mph — it's not as simple as calculating a vehicle's miles-per-gallon (or gallons-per-mile) rating. Railroads generally rate locomotives by horsepower hours per gallon (HPHG).

As an example, a common road engine of the 1970s to 2000s, the 3,000-hp SD40-2, burns about 5 gallons per hour (GPH) while idling. This jumps to 57 GPH in notch 4, 108 GPH in notch 6, and 165 GPH in notch 8 (full throttle). At full throttle, this means about 17 horsepower-hours per gallon. This usage jumps to about 210 GPH at full throttle for a modern 4,400-hp engine, but with better efficiency (about 20 HPHG).

"wet" system, where water is always routed through the radiator; GE uses what is known as a "dry" system, where — although there is always water in the radiator — cooling water is routed through radiators only as needed. Both now use what is known as "split cooling" — valves control how much water is routed based on operating temperature: some water passes directly through, but other water passes through another radiator section ("subcooler" or "aftercooler") to further lower the temperature. This water is then routed to the oil cooler and to cool engine intake air after it has been compressed by the turbocharger.

Fuel tank equipment includes, from upper left, an emergency fuel shutoff switch, dial-style fuel gauge, fuel filler with cap, and fuel-level sight glass. *Cody Grivno*

Many modern locomotives have external digital fuel gauges. This is on an EMD SD70ACe, with the emergency fuel cutoff button to the right. *Jim Wrinn*

Inertial air filter system (EMD GP30)

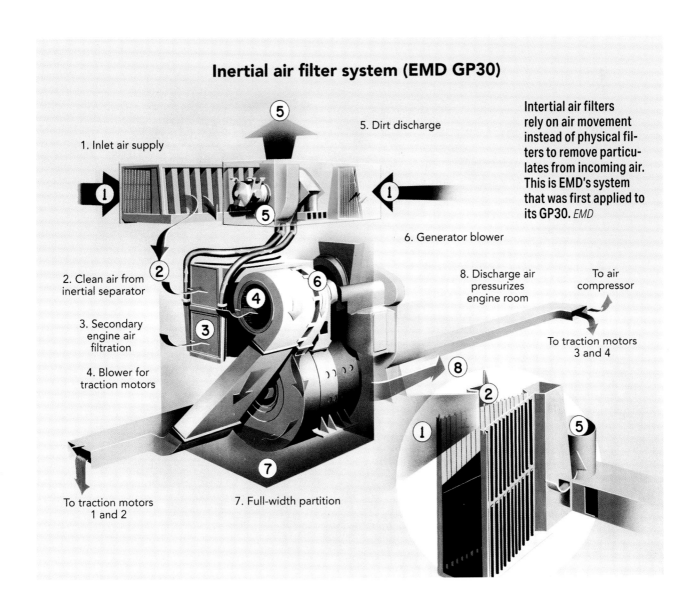

1. Inlet air supply

5. Dirt discharge

Intertial air filters rely on air movement instead of physical filters to remove particulates from incoming air. This is EMD's system that was first applied to its GP30. *EMD*

6. Generator blower

2. Clean air from inertial separator

3. Secondary engine air filtration

4. Blower for traction motors

8. Discharge air pressurizes engine room

To air compressor

To traction motors 3 and 4

To traction motors 1 and 2

7. Full-width partition

HORSEPOWER, BRAKE HORSEPOWER, AND TRACTIVE EFFORT

Determining the power and strength of a locomotive is a lot more than simply knowing its horsepower rating. Understanding horsepower and tractive effort (TE) and how they vary by speed will help explain how a seemingly diminutive 660-hp switcher can walk away with a string of 80 cars in a yard — the same cut of cars that took three 1,500-hp road locomotives to carry from a neighboring division point 150 miles away.

Tractive effort is the pulling force in pounds exerted by a locomotive. It's a calculated based on horsepower, weight on driving wheels, gear ratio, speed, and estimated factor of adhesion. Drawbar pull is the actual force applied at the rear coupler of the locomotive, and can be measured by a dynamometer car. Tractive effort is at its highest at slow speed when a locomotive is starting, and drops as speed increases.

Horsepower for a diesel locomotive is calculated by the power generated by the engine and the output in watts (voltage x amperes) of the generator or alternator. Since the resistance of a train increases as speed increases, the faster a train needs to go, the more horsepower that's required.

The chart at right shows sample TE curves for three locomotives: an EMD SD38-2 (six axles, 2,000 hp), a drag-freight engine of the 1970s; an EMD F40PH (four axles, 3,000 hp; the most-common high-speed passenger locomotive of the 1970s-early 2000s), and a modern GE ES44AC (six-axle, 4,400 hp) AC-traction-motor freight locomotive. For all, note that TE is

highest at low speeds. The straight horizontal lines at the far left of the chart for the SD38-2 and F40PH indicate that their starting TE is limited by adhesion. The ES44AC has much higher TE starting and throughout its speed range, both because of its higher output and because its microprocessor control and AC traction motors give it a higher factor of adhesion (more on that in Chapter 4).

"Brake horsepower" refers to the total horsepower output of an engine. All of an engine's power does not make it to the traction motors. Other systems, including the auxiliary generator (which supplies electrical and electronic control devices), blowers, and head-end power (on passenger locomotives so equipped) also use some of the engine's power (referred to as "parasitic loss"). Thus, a modern locomotive

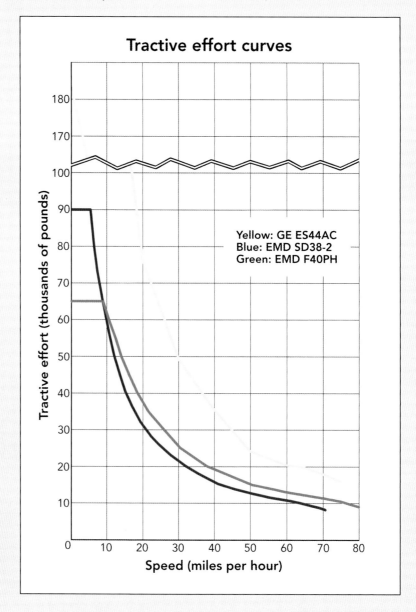

Tractive effort curves

Yellow: GE ES44AC
Blue: EMD SD38-2
Green: EMD F40PH

may put out 4,600 brake horsepower, but be rated at 4,400 hp because that's what is available for traction.

So the simplified answer to our switcher vs. road locomotive question is that tractive effort is what's important when starting and when pulling heavy loads at slow speeds. Horsepower is what's needed for moving trains at high speed. Our 660-hp switcher can pull a long cut of cars on a level yard track at 6 mph. However, it took the combined 4,500 hp of three road locomotives to move the cars at 50 mph on the main line while overcoming rolling resistance, grades, curves, wind, and other factors.

Railroads extensively test their locomotives to see how much they can pull in various situations. They publish tonnage ratings, listing how many horsepower per ton is required for operating districts (or for individual trains). The chart on page 165 in Chapter 8 shows how modern locomotives provide computer analysis of tractive effort and adhesion in real time.

Operating trains at high speeds requires more horsepower, which means more locomotives and more fuel. Running freight trains above 50 mph not only requires more fuel, but also causes more wear to wheels, brake shoes, and the track structure. It also requires additional braking power and longer stopping distances, creating more operating hazards.

Because of this, railroads have largely found that, with rare exceptions, it's generally better to focus on keeping freight trains moving rather than moving them at high speeds. In other words, expediting yard switching and limiting terminal time for cars is more effective at efficient train movement than simple speed.

In general, the larger the engine, the more cooling that's needed; this is why radiator sections became noticeably larger on high-horsepower engines by the 1970s (visible in the flared grilles on EMD's SD45 and the large radiator wings on GE's U33 and U36 models). Since cooling is an important part of emission control, modern locomotives have large radiator cores with multiple sections, protruding prominently from the rear roof.

Fuel system

Diesel locomotive engines burn diesel fuel (No. 2 diesel fuel). Diesel was once far cheaper than gasoline, as it requires less initial refining. However, recent years have seen diesel prices rising because of extra processing that significantly lowers the sulfur content — critical to lowering volatile emissions as well as limiting engine wear — and the paraffin content. The precise blend of fuel and various additives is adjusted by season, with different blends for winter and summer.

Locomotives have large fuel tanks. Switchers typically have 600-gallon tanks, with 1,200- to 3,500-gallon tanks on most road locomotives through the 1970s. Modern diesels have 4,000- to 5,600-gallon fuel tanks.

Like oil and water, the fuel system is closed; any leaking or cross-contamination among the three systems can be a serious problem. A pump draws fuel from the bottom of the tank and starts it on its way in the fuel line at a pressure of 35 to 45 pounds per square inch. The fuel line passes through a fuel strainer and filters. The fuel is then heated and sent to the engine, where it is routed to the injectors. Along with burning in the cylinders, fuel is used to cool and lubricate the injectors. This excess fuel is recaptured and routed back to the tank. Locomotives equipped with steam generators (passenger locomotives into the 1970s) have a fuel line to the generator as well.

On each side of the fuel tank are one or

two sight glasses that show the physical fuel level, and most tanks also have a dial-type gauge (some contemporary locomotives have digital gauges). There will also be a filler spout (with a red cap), along with an emergency fuel cutoff button (labeled, with a red housing): pushing that switch turns off the fuel pump. Fuel tanks also have drain valves, allowing water (condensation) that has accumulated to be drawn off.

Engine air

A significant amount of air is required for engine combustion, for cooling the radiator, and — on most locomotives since the 1960s — for pressurizing the engine room and electrical cabinets. Compressed air is also required for the brake system and other ancillary gear, such as horns (see more on that in Chapters 7 and 9).

Engines require a tremendous volume of air for combustion, especially at full speed. This air must be filtered to keep it free of particulates that could damage cylinders and other internal engine components. Most early diesels did this using oil-bath filters, which, as the description sounds, used oil to grab particulates. This type of fileter required frequent maintenance. Paper filters were used on some locomotives, and although they work well, needed frequent replacement.

An innovation in the 1960s was the inertial filter. This is a box or cylinder that

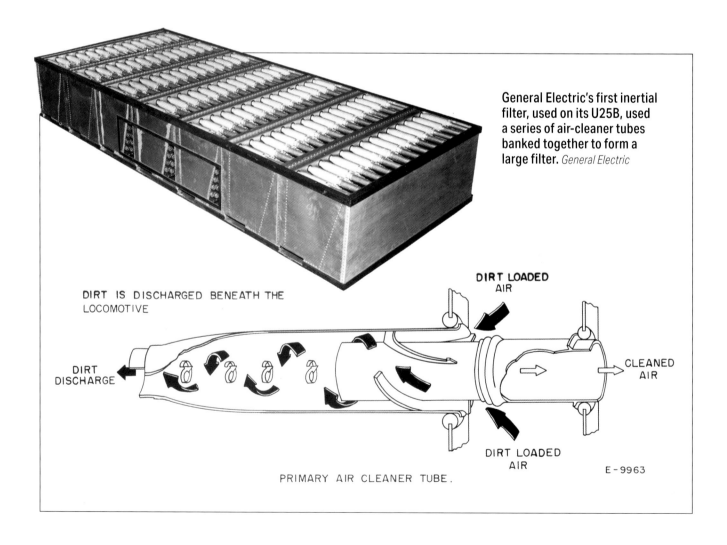

General Electric's first inertial filter, used on its U25B, used a series of air-cleaner tubes banked together to form a large filter. *General Electric*

EPA TIER 4 STANDARDS

With Environmental Protection Agency Tier 4 emission regulations in effect since 2015, new locomotives must meet these standards. Tier 4 is the culmination of a multi-decade program designed to slowly decrease oxides of nitrogen, particulate matter, hydrocarbons, and carbon monoxide in exhaust. Tier 0 covers locomotives built between 1973 and 2001; Tier 1, 2002-2004; Tier 2, 2005-2011; Tier 3, 2012-2014; and Tier 4, 2015-today. Regulations provide different emission standards for line-haul and switch locomotives to differentiate between locomotives and their typical duty cycles. While significant differences exist between the two earlier tier levels, at Tier 4, line-haul and switch locomotive standards are essentially the same.

Four technologies are in use, and while they can be used to treat exhaust singly or in combinations, no solution uses all four. Exhaust aftertreatment is just part of the complex puzzle that engine manufacturers must solve to achieve emission compliance.

Engines can be tuned to emit different levels of each pollutant for treatment. Often adjusting the engine to address one pollutant can adversely affect another. For example, tuning an engine to a hotter combustion temperature reduces the particulate matter but increases nitrous oxide. Cooler combustion temperatures have an inverse effect. Here are the four complex processes that are used to reduce engine pollutants.

DOC (Diesel Oxidation Catalyst) — A diesel oxidation catalyst chamber is installed on top of the turbocharger and is primarily used to reduce carbon monoxide and hydrocarbons, but is ineffective at reducing particulate matter and nitrogen oxide. It is commonly used in conjunction with other solutions for the other pollutants.

DPF (Diesel Particulate Filter) — This reduces particulate matter by trapping it in filters. Buildup of particulate matter in the filter can cause a reduction of engine performance. One way trapped particulate matter can be burned is by passing hot exhaust gases through the filter in a process called passive regeneration. The filter also accumulates ash from engine oil burned in the cylinders, and requires periodic removal and cleaning.

EGR (Exhaust Gas Recirculation) — While not technically an aftertreatment, it's a recirculation system that takes a portion of the exhaust gas, cools it, and routes it back into the air intake where it's mixed with fresh air for combustion again. The lower oxygen content of the recirculated air reduces the amount of nitrogen oxide created by the engine. Both EMD (1010J engine) and Wabtec (GEVO) use EGR for their freight locomotives.

SCR (Selective Catalytic Reduction) — This system requires an additive fluid called DEF, a urea and water solution, which is sprayed into the exhaust before entering the catalyst. When the solution mixes with the hot exhaust gas, it's converted to ammonia and reacts with catalysts to reduce the nitrogen oxide. While this system reduces some hydrocarbons, carbon monoxide, and particulate matter, it's most effective at reducing nitrogen oxide. The urea and water solution must be stored on the locomotive to avoid extreme temperatures. An engine with this system uses approximately one-half to 1 gallon of urea and water solution for every 10 gallons of diesel fuel burned. Most new passenger locomotives use SCR. — *Chris Guss (originally published in* Trains, *February 2017)*

sets up incoming air in a controlled swirl; particulate matter is separated, removed from the air current, and ejected from the filter box. Thus no physical filter is needed.

Starting with GE's U25B in 1959, it became standard to lightly pressurize engine compartments. This helps keep external dust and particulates from entering any gaps in engineroom doors, keeping the engine room cleaner. Electrical cabinets are also pressurized with low-pressure air to keep out dust and dirt.

Locomotive side walls have a variety of grilles, screens, shutters, and vents to pass air in and out. Their exact placement and use varies widely by manufacturer, era, and model.

The next chapter looks at several notable diesel engine designs.

CHAPTER 3

NOTABLE DIESEL ENGINE DESIGNS

How the manufacturers took the same basic diesel concepts and developed engines to power locomotives

A new Alco model 244 engine has been installed on the frame of an RS2 under construction at Alco's Schenectady plant in the late 1940s. The worker in the hood is installing a clutch for the radiator fan drive, while two other employees install gear on the end platform. *Alco*

53

Although diesel engines all operate in the same basic manner, each manufacturer takes a different approach in designing them. Every design is a balancing act between power, weight, efficiency, durability, ease of maintenance, and for modern locomotives, managing emissions. Some engines remained in production for decades; others didn't fare well at all, and some ultimately were responsible for the failure of the locomotive companies that produced them.

As diesel engine technology evolved and power output increased from the 1940s onward, manufacturers were repeatedly faced with a decision: Try to push more power from an existing engine, or develop a new design. Ultimately, new designs were needed to achieve the power, fuel efficiency, and environmental standards needed for today's 4,400-hp AC-traction diesels.

The following summaries highlight the most notable engines used in diesel-electric locomotives since the 1930s. The size,

power, key benefits, challenges, and problem areas for each are highlighted. You won't find highly technical descriptions here — entire books and reports have been written to explain, in detailed mechanical terms, how many of these engines were designed.

We'll start with a look at Electro-Motive engines, then move to Alco, General Electric/Wabtec, and other builders.

Electro-Motive Corporation, Electro-Motive Division, Electro-Motive Diesel
Winton 201A

General Motors acquired the Electro-Motive Corp. and the Winton Engine Co. in 1930, providing Winton with the financial and other resources needed to develop a new diesel engine design. The result was the Winton 201A, a two-cycle, non-turbocharged engine that was built in six- and eight-cylinder in-line versions and 12- and 16-cylinder V-style versions with horsepower ratings from 600 to 1,200 hp. It was the first successful two-cycle design,

The original Winton 201A engine from Burlington's *Pioneer Zephyr* of 1934, an in-line eight-cylinder version, had been pulled from that train, reconditioned, and re-installed in a switcher. Upon that locomotive's retirement and trade-in, EMD donated the historic engine to the Smithsonian Institution for display. *Smithsonian Institution*

Most common diesel engines have been built in varying sizes to suit different locomotive types. This early six-cylinder EMD 567 engine was used in the company's 600-hp SW1 switchers. *EMD*

and its greatest asset for rail use was its light weight for its power output compared to other engines of the period. Development began in 1932, and a pair of 8-cylinder versions were displayed at the Chicago World's Fair in 1933-1934, where they powered the GM display at the Century of Progress exhibition.

The initial 201 used a fabricated block (weldment) with separate power assemblies (mainly the cylinder head assembly) and components, and a then-revolutionary compact fuel injector. The engine had an 8-inch bore and 10-inch stroke, with a 502-cubic-inch displacement per cylinder. The V-style engine had a 60-degree angle between banks of cylinders (making it wider and shorter than the later 567 engine).

An improved version, the 201A, would find success in powering most early streamliners of the 1930s, including the first diesel-electric streamliner, the Chicago, Burlington & Quincy's *Zephyr*, in 1934. The six- and eight-cylinder versions powered EMC's new line of switchers, pairs of 12-cylinder 201As were used in early E units (EA, E1, E2), and 16-cylinder versions were used in some streamliner power cars.

Although revolutionary and reasonably successful, the design suffered from a variety of issues (cylinder head problems, chronic leaks in various systems). Instead of revising the design, EMC chose to develop an all-new, more-powerful design in 1939. Most Winton-engined locomotives were retired or re-engined by the late 1950s.

EMD 567

Electro-Motive took what it learned from the Winton 201A and developed an all-new engine design, the 567 (named for the cubic-inch displacement of each cylinder). It was an immediate success, offering more power than the 201A with higher reliability.

The 567 engine block is a weldment, with separate power assembly components to simplify maintenance. It's a V-style engine with cylinders at a 45-degree angle, making it taller and narrower than the 201A. It has an 8½-inch bore and 10-inch stroke, and engine speed ranges from 180 rpm at idle to 800 rpm at full throttle (900 rpm on later versions). It has overhead camshafts, one per cylinder bank (the earlier Winton engines were a push-rod design with a lower camshaft). The 567 is normally aspirated (using a Roots blower),

Electro-Motive's 567 engines lend themselves well to reconditioning and rebuilding. Here workers change out power assemblies (several of which are on the pallet at right) on a 16-cylinder version. *EMD*

but turbocharging became an option with the GP20/SD24 starting in 1958.

With more than 24,000 installed in new locomotives, the 567 became the most-successful and widely used locomotive engine of all time, noted for its durability and ease of repair and maintenance. It was the standard EMD engine beginning with the streamlined passenger E3 in 1938 (twin 12-cylinder engines) and successive E units. The FT of 1939 and successive freight locomotives used single 16-cylinder engines, while switchers of various power ratings used 6- 8-, and 12-cylinder 567s.

The 567's features were continually upgraded to increase reliability and eliminate issues such as leaks and cracking, with improved lube oil plumbing, cylinder liners, manifold, and other components. Major revisions were indicated by suffix letters to indicate the crankcase design; the final version was the 567D series, which

used a heavier crankcase to support the turbochargers that were introduced in 1959.

The last locomotives to use the 567 were the GP35/SD35 series, which ended production in 1966, closing out 28 years of the design. Additionally, the 567's design lent itself to rebuilding, and many 567-engined locomotives — especially GP7s and GP9s — had their engines rebuilt during the 1960s, 1970s, or 1980s, with some still in service.

EMD 645

By the time the 2,500-hp GP35 and SD35 were in production, the 567 engine had reached its practical power limit. To increase output, EMD took the basic 567 design, widened the cylinder bore to $9\frac{1}{16}$ inches, and upgraded other components. The result was the 645, also named for its cylinder displacement. It was still built in normally aspirated (Roots-blown) and turbocharged versions. Following testing,

the first production locomotives with the 645 appeared in 1965: the 3,000-hp GP40/SD40 series (16-cylinder, turbocharged), 3,600-hp SD45 (20-cylinder, turbocharged), and 2,000-hp GP38/SD38 (16-cylinder, non-turbocharged). Eight- and 12-cylinder versions were used in switchers. As a major player in the then-escalating "horsepower race" among builders, EMD's 645-engined offerings would become extremely popular and successful.

The 645 engine has a higher maximum speed than the 567: 900 rpm, with 950 rpm on the 20-cylinder SD45. The 16-cylinder version weighs just over 18 tons. The engine, with upgrades, remained in use in EMD's popular Dash-2 line through the 1970s, along with the SW1000, SW1500, and MP15 switchers.

The last use of the 16-cylinder version was the 16-645F3B on EMD's 3,600-hp GP50/SD50 series from 1980 to 1987.

However, as EMD tried to get more power from the 16-cylinder version, the SD50 suffered from a higher rate of engine and power-assembly failures and maintenance issues than the earlier — and notably reliable — '40-series locomotives. The '50-series' continuing problems led to a drop in sales, contributing to GE snatching the locomotive sales lead from EMD in 1987. A new, larger engine was again needed.

EMD 710

The 710 was a progression of the earlier 645 design, keeping the same 9¹/₁₆-inch bore as the 645 but with an 11-inch stroke (710-cubic-inch displacement). It was still a two-cycle engine, but the first that was only available with a turbocharger. It debuted in 1984 in the 3,800-hp SD60/GP60 series and was built in 12-, 16-, and 20-cylinder versions, with output up to 5,000 hp for the 20-cylinder model (in the SD80MAC). The

The EMD 645 engine, which debuted in the mid-1960s, was based on the same design as the 567, but with larger cylinders (78 cubic inches more of displacement). This is the 20-cylinder version of the 645 that powers EMD's 3,600-hp SD45. The turbo is at top left.
EMD

The model 710, which succeeded the 645, was EMD's last two-cycle engine design. Here a 710 is being installed on the frame of an SD70-series locomotive under construction at the London, Ontario assembly plant.
David Lustig

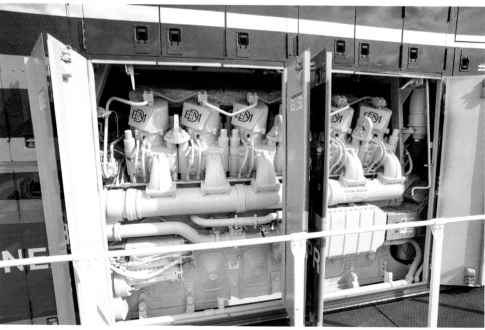

Electro-Motive Diesel's 1010J engine, a four-cycle, three-turbocharger design, is the company's method of meeting Tier 4 emissions standards. The tops of the power assemblies are readily visible in this view of the engine room of demonstrator SD70ACe-T4 No. 1501.
Jim Wrinn

"standard" version is the 16-cylinder, 3,800-4,500-hp version used in '60- and '70-series locomotives. A 12-cylinder version was used in the F59PH and other similar passenger diesels (3,000 hp). The engine, as with its predecessors, was upgraded and increased in power through production, from the 4,000-hp early SD70 series to the 4,300- and 4,500-hp AC-traction SD70ACe.

The 710 had some teething problems but soon earned a reliable reputation, eventually becoming EMD's longest-running domestic engine (1984-2014). Even though it had become a reliable, trusted design, it could not be easily reconfigured to comply with the stringent Tier 4 emissions standards that took effect on Jan. 1, 2015. This effectively ended its use domestically, although it continues to be used in export locomotives.

EMD 265H, 1010J

The all-new 265H was a radical departure for EMD, not only because of its size and increased power output, but it was also EMD's first four-cycle engine. Development began in 1994. It was a completely new design, developed to power the 6,000-hp SD90MAC. The 265H — nicknamed the "H-engine" — has a 265mm (10.4 inch) bore and 300 mm (12 inch) stroke (1,010-cubic-inch per cylinder displacement) and a top speed of 1,000

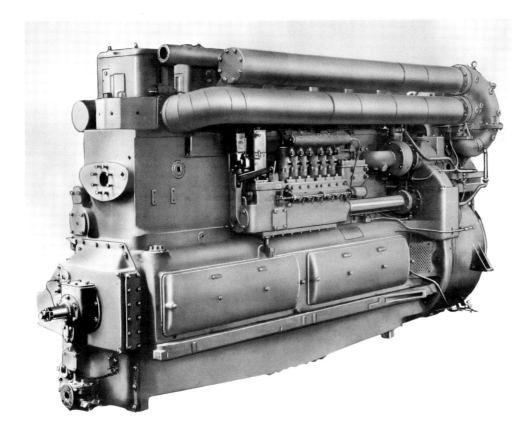

Alco's six-cylinder in-line 539 engine powered the company's early switchers and pioneering RS1 road switcher. The generator is at the far end. *Alco*

rpm. The engine has a cast-iron crankcase (previous EMD designs were weldments), two turbochargers (one per cylinder bank), electronic fuel injection, and redesigned camshafts, pistons, and cylinders.

The first applications, as 16-cylinder engines in SD90MACs, were delivered in 1996. The locomotive and engine design were, however, unsuccessful. The locomotives had numerous reliability issues, and railroads largely discovered that the increased power wasn't worth the loss of flexibility that lower-horsepower engines allowed. The last were built in 2000, as railroads continued buying SD70-series locomotives with 710 engines.

With the coming of Tier 4 standards in 2015, EMD engineers initially tried to redesign the 710 engine to be compliant, but were unable to do so practically. Instead, designers went back to the four-cycle idea of the 265H. They kept the basic engine size (bore, stroke, and 1,010-cubic-inch displacement) but redesigned everything else to eliminate problems with the previous engine. The result was the 1010J ("J-engine"). It was designed in conjunction with Caterpillar, which owns Progress Rail, which acquired EMD in 2010.

To meet emissions standards, the 12-cylinder 1010J uses exhaust gas recirculation (EGR), in which exhaust gases are cooled and reflow back through the combustion cycle. Enabling this is two-stage turbocharging, which the engine accomplishes via three turbochargers (one high-pressure turbo and a pair of low-pressure turbos). The resulting locomotive is the 4,400-hp (4,600-hp brake horsepower, with 4,400 used for traction) SD70ACe-T4.

Caterpillar C175

The Cat C175 is a high-speed, four-cycle diesel engine with a top speed of 1,800

The Alco 244 engine provided more power than the 539, but it was rushed into production and suffered from multiple reliability issues. This is a 12-cylinder version; the turbocharger is at upper right and the generator at far left. *Alco*

rpm. It's a V-style design with a 6.89-inch bore and 8.66-inch stroke. The 20-cylinder version of the C175 has powered EMD's 4,000-hp F125 (Spirit) passenger locomotives since 2015. The engine is lightweight (about 11 tons) and is Tier 4 compliant, using an exhaust after-treatment (SCR, selective catalytic reduction) system.

American Locomotive Co. (Alco) McIntosh & Seymour 531

Alco, after leaving the partnership with GE and Ingersoll-Rand that produced boxcab switchers in the 1920s, acquired engine-builder McIntosh & Seymour in 1929. The first result of this was the 531 engine, a six-cylinder in-line design with a 12½-inch bore and 13-inch stroke. Alco named engines for the bore designation (first digit), followed by the year it was developed (last two digits). The 531 developed 600 hp (non-turbocharged) or 900 hp

(turbocharged 531T). It was a tall engine, and its main use was in Alco's HH (high-hood) switchers, named for the hood, which reached to the top level of the cab roof. The 531 was discontinued with the development of the 538/539 designs in 1938.

539

The 539 engine was a modification to the earlier 538, which itself was a replacement for the earlier 531 design. Its major revision was that the base of the engine rested below the frame, allowing a lower hood than the HH switchers. The 539 used a cast block and was, like the earlier engines, an in-line six-cylinder design with a 12½-inch bore and 13-inch stroke. Speed ranged from 315 rpm at idle to 740 rpm at full throttle. Non-turbo versions were used in Alco's S1 and S3 switchers, with a 660-hp rating. The turbocharged (539T) 1,000-hp version was used in the S2 and S4

switchers (1,000 hp), RS1 road switchers, and DL-series passenger locomotives. The 539 remained Alco's low-horsepower engine through the 1950s.

241, 244

Alco's first attempt at a more-powerful engine for road locomotives was the 241, with design and experimental work from 1940 to 1944. Several problems developed — exacerbated by World War II restrictions — that led to its abandonment and the development of a new design, the 244.

The 244 is a turbocharged, V-style (45-degree cylinder banks), four-cycle engine with a 9-inch bore and 10½-inch stroke. It was built in 12-cylinder versions for freight locomotives (1,500- and 1,600-hp) and 16-cylinder for passenger service in PAs (2,000- and 2,250 hp). A 16-cylinder version was also used in the six-axle RSD7 road switcher (2,400 hp).

The design was rushed into production following the failure of the 241 design to meet a backlog of locomotive orders as wartime production restrictions were eased, and from its first deliveries in 1946, the 244 suffered from a variety of problems involving crankshafts, turbochargers, and the engine blocks themselves. Many industry experts blame the 244 engine for Alco's drop in locomotive sales and eventual exit from the market. Although improvements were made to the engine and many of its early problems were solved during production, by the time the revised 244D emerged in 1950, many railroads were turning away from Alco locomotive designs.

251

With the 244 engine experiencing many problems, Alco decided to replace it with an all-new design. The company began work on the 251 engine design in

A 12-cylinder Alco 251 engine is lowered onto the frame of a new road switcher at the Schenectady plant in 1958. The 251 was a much-improved and more-dependable design compared to the problematic 244. *Alco*

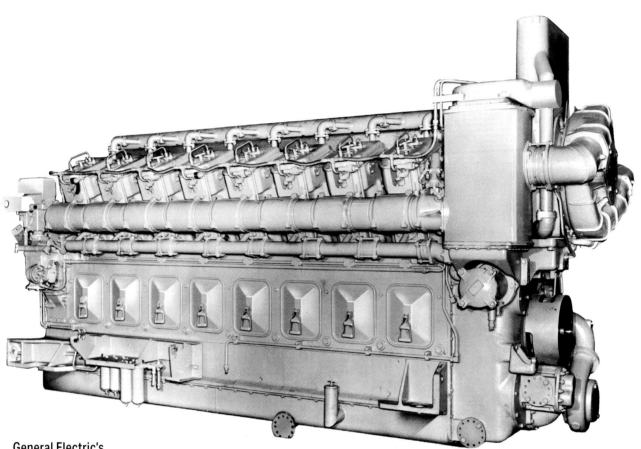

General Electric's road switchers were powered by various versions of its 7FDL engine from 1960 into the 2000s. This is a 16-cylinder version destined for a U25B in 1962. *General Electric*

1949. It kept the same bore and stroke of the 244 (9 inches x 10½ inches) and was also a four-stroke, turbocharged engine, but with improved engine block cooling, revised power assembly components, and the addition of an intercooler for the turbocharger. It was built both in an in-line 6-cylinder version (for various 800- to 1,000-hp switchers) and a V-engine with 8, 12, 16, and 18 cylinders.

The first applications of the 251 were in the RS11/RSD12 road switchers in 1956. Reliability and performance were much improved over the 244, and the 251 earned a reputation as a solid design, but it wasn't enough to revive Alco sales and keep the company in the locomotive business. The 251 — with upgrades — remained Alco's primary engine through the end of the company's locomotive production in 1969 and through subsequent Montreal Locomotive Works

and Bombardier production. The 251's last North American locomotive use was in Bombardier's HR616, 20 six-axle cowl locomotives built for Canadian National in 1982 (251E engine, 3,000 hp). Alco-designed engines are still produced as of 2023 by Fairbanks-Morse (another company whose engines long outlived its locomotive manufacturing business).

General Electric, Wabtec 7FDL

For its popular small switchers of the 1940s and 1950s, General Electric relied on small diesel engines from Caterpillar (44-tonner) and Cooper-Bessemer (70-tonner). The 16-cylinder 7FDL engine that powered GE's first high-horsepower road switcher, the 2,500-hp U25B of 1959, originated as a Cooper-Bessemer design. GE shortly acquired the rights to it and began

building the engine in 12- and 16-cylinder versions (7FDL12, 7FDL16). It's a four-cycle, V-style (45-degree) turbocharged engine with a 9-inch bore and 10½-inch stroke. Engine speed ranges from 450 rpm at idle to 1,050 rpm at full throttle. In GE nomenclature: 7 = power-generating engine; F = 9-inch bore; D = engine configuration indicator; L = locomotive use; followed by number of cylinders.

GE continued upgrading the 7FDL design, using versions of it in all of its locomotives through the Dash 9 and AC locomotive series into 2004. Early versions (on the U25B and U25C) generated 2,500 hp, increasing to 4,400 hp on the Dash 9-44C and AC4400CW.

GE/Wabtec 7HDL, GEVO

In 1995, GE introduced the 7HDL16A, a higher-power engine designed for its

6,000-hp AC6000CW. The 16-cylinder engines, built in conjunction with Germany's Deutz-MWM, produced 6,250 brake horsepower (6,000 hp for traction). The 7HDL had a larger bore and stroke (9.8 inches x 12.6 inches) than the FDL, and was a four-cycle, twin-turbocharged design. The engine, like EMD's 265H, suffered from problems regarding durability of components, and that — and a lack of flexibility of 6,000-hp locomotives — led to the end of AC6000CW production in 2001, with just over 300 built.

General Electric (which was purchased by Wabtec in 2019) revised the design and used it as the basis for its Tier-4 compliant engine, the GEVO. The new engine, in 12- and 16-cylinder versions, has the same basic specifications as the HDL, but with upgraded materials throughout the power assembly. The 12-cylinder version

The standard engine on all GE/Wabtec domestic freight locomotives is the GEVO. Here a 12-cylinder version is paired with an alternator on a cart at GE's Fort Worth, Texas, plant in 2013. *Chris Guss*

63

This Baldwin RF16 "shark" cab unit is powered by a turbocharged 608A engine, an eight-cylinder in-line design. This view is from the rear of the engine room toward the cab (the door to the cab is up the steps at the end of the aisle at left).

Jim Shaughnessy

is standard on Wabtec's current 4,400-hp, Tier-4-compliant ES44AC.

Baldwin
De La Vergne VO and 600

After experimenting with boxcab diesels in the 1920s, Baldwin acquired the De La Vergne Engine Co. in 1931 with the goal of producing a standard line of diesel-electric locomotives. The first engine specifically designed for large locomotives was the VO in 1935. It was an in-line six-cylinder, four-cycle engine with a 12½-inch bore and 15½-inch stroke, and produced 660 hp. It was a slow-speed engine, with a top speed of 600 rpm. In 1937 an eight-cylinder, 900-hp version was added. It became standard for the company's switchers. The design was revised in 1939 with a larger bore (12¾ inches), bumping the eight-cylinder model to 1,000 hp.

Baldwin revised and re-engineered the design in 1945. The cylinder heads (and pistons as well) had to be redesigned to allow turbocharging, as the VO's offset combustion chamber didn't allow it. The new 600-series engines were available normally aspirated (NA) or turbocharged (SC, for "supercharger") in six-cylinder (606NA, 606SC) and eight-cylinder (608NA, 608SC) versions, with power rating up to 1,500 hp for the 608SC. It was still a slow-speed in-line engine, with a top speed of 625 rpm.

In 1950 the design was upgraded to the 600A, with the same basic specs but a larger-diameter crankshaft and other improvements, with a 1,600 hp rating for the turbocharged 608A.

Engine problems plagued many Baldwin locomotives, including engine-block cracks and leaks and piston failures and leaks. The 608A helped reliability, but earlier problems, plus Baldwin's status as a minority builder, led to decreasing sales for the company by the 1950s. The company ceased building locomotives in 1956, and many of its locomotives (especially road engines) were retired by the late 1960s.

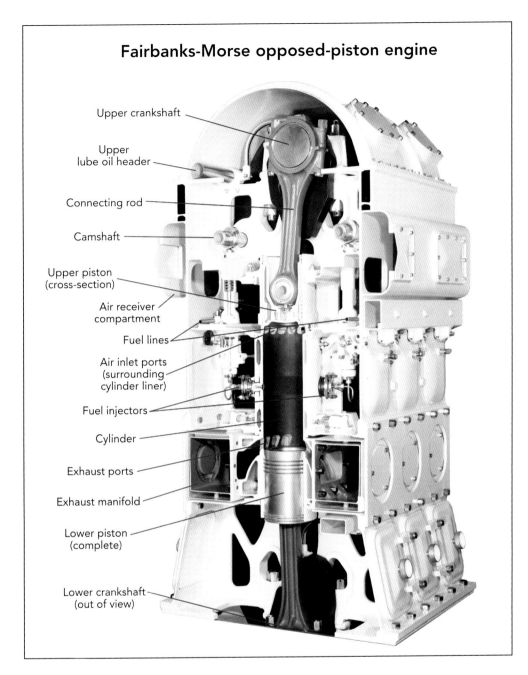

Fairbanks-Morse opposed-piston engine

- Upper crankshaft
- Upper lube oil header
- Connecting rod
- Camshaft
- Upper piston (cross-section)
- Air receiver compartment
- Fuel lines
- Air inlet ports (surrounding cylinder liner)
- Fuel injectors
- Cylinder
- Exhaust ports
- Exhaust manifold
- Lower piston (complete)
- Lower crankshaft (out of view)

This cross-section view of a Fairbanks-Morse opposed-piston Model 38 8⅛ diesel shows the upper and lower crankshaft and illustrates how two pistons share the same cylinder. Fuel injectors are in the middle, with air inlet and exhaust ports both regulated by piston movement. *Fairbanks-Morse*

Fairbanks-Morse
Opposed-piston model 38 8⅛

The most radical engine design in locomotives was the Fairbanks-Morse opposed-piston (OP) engine. The OP eliminated the cylinder head by placing two pistons in each cylinder, with a crankshaft both above and below the cylinder bank The crankshafts are married at one end via gears and a vertical shaft. The FM OP was used extensively in marine operations, and FM began building locomotives with it as a way of expanding its market.

The OP Model 38 is a two-cycle, Roots-blown engine with a 8⅛-inch bore and 10-inch stroke for each piston in each cylinder. The piston cranks for each pair of pistons are offset by 12 degrees so that pistons in each opposed pair are never both at dead center when at their extreme outer positions. The engine has no air intake or exhaust valves, instead relying on fixed ports around the cylinder liners — the pistons open and close the ports as they travel over them. This made the OP an overall simpler design compared to a conventional engine, and

This artist's rendering shows a Lima-Hamilton T89SA eight-cylinder turbocharged in-line engine. It was innovative for its intercooler, water-cooled exhaust manifold, and dry-sump lubricating oil system. *Lima-Hamilton*

increased the efficiency. The 38 was built in several sizes (6-, 8-, 10-, and 12-cylinder), providing from 1,000 to 2,400 hp.

The major selling point of the OP was that the design produced more power compared to a similar-size conventional diesel. When in good working order, they provided outstanding service; FM switchers in particular had reputations as excellent lugging locomotives, and the 2,400-hp Train Master (H24-66), the highest-horsepower road switcher of its time, was known for its power and fast acceleration.

The engines, however, often proved to be headaches in locomotive service. Major maintenance on the power assembly components required pulling not just a cylinder head, but removing the locomotive hood and entire top crankshaft — a major time investment. Operationally, the volume of air and cooling required caused

problems at higher altitudes and in high-temperature situations, and excess heat in the lower pistons and cylinders were also an issue. Although FM exited the locomotive business in the late 1950s, the company still produces OP engines for other uses.

Lima-Hamilton
T69SA, T89SA

Lima's foray into diesels was brief and too late to become more than a footnote in diesel history. Lima partnered with engine-builder Hamilton in 1947 and turned out its first locomotive, a switcher, in 1949. The company's six- and eight-cylinder engines (T69SA, 1,000 hp; T89SA, 1,200 hp) were in-line, four-cycle turbocharged designs. They were based on a Hamilton design dating to the mid-1930s. In Hamilton terminology: T = turbocharged; the two digits are number of cylinders and the

The Cummins QSK95 is a high-speed (1,200-rpm), 16-cylinder V-style engine. The Tier 4-compliant engine (using selective catalytic reduction aftertreatment) is most notably used by Siemens to power its Charger series of passenger locomotives.
David Lustig

cylinder bore in inches; SA = "single acting" (firing at top of piston only).

The engine used a welded steel (A-frame) block, forged aluminum pistons, and a 9-inch bore and 12-inch stroke with a 950 rpm top speed. The engine was the first locomotive diesel to use an intercooler (which cools combustion air after it has been compressed by a turbocharger) and a water-cooled exhaust manifold. It used a dry-sump oil system (with multiple pumps and reservoirs).

Although the engine had some novel design elements, the company simply wasn't around long enough to leave much of an impression on the industry. Lima-Hamilton built only 174 total locomotives before its line was discontinued upon merger into Baldwin in 1951. Most lasted in service through the mid to late 1960s.

Siemens
Cummins QSK95

The QSK95, built by Cummins, is a high-speed (1,200-rpm) 16-cylinder, V-style diesel used by Siemens in its Charger line (ALC-42 and others) of high-speed passenger locomotives beginning in 2016. The QSK95 has a cast iron block, forged-steel pistons, rods, and crankshaft, and has two-stage aftercooling with four single-stage turbochargers. Cylinders have a 7.48-inch bore and 8.27-inch stroke, producing 4,000 to 4,400 hp. The engine is EPA Tier 4 compliant using SCR (selective catalytic reduction aftertreatment) for emissions.

CHAPTER 4

ELECTRICAL EQUIPMENT

From miles of wire to sophisticated computer components, a diesel locomotive relies on electricity to do its job

Taking the motion of the diesel engine and converting it into energy to turn the wheels is the job of the generator, alternator, traction motors, and a variety of other electrical and electronic gear. The result is an electric transmission — what makes all modern diesel locomotives "diesel-electrics."

Locomotives have multiple low-voltage electrical systems that control everything from headlights to sensors and fans. Modern locomotives also have extensive microprocessor and computer systems that control and monitor a variety of functions and locomotive systems.

Let's start by examining the high-voltage traction system and see how the components have evolved and improved over time, notably the shift from DC to AC traction motors. Then, we'll look at locomotives' low-voltage systems and see how electronics come to play a larger role in many aspects of locomotive operation.

A worker secures field coils in a generator under construction at EMD in the 1960s. By 1940, Electro-Motive was building its own electrical components to avoid depending upon outside vendors such as GE and Westinghouse. *EMD*

Electric transmission

The main generator (alternator from the mid-1960s onward) is powered by the engine's crankshaft. As Chapter 2 explained, the engine's rotational speed is controlled by the engineer's throttle settings. The higher the throttle setting, the faster the generator turns and the more power that is generated. This electricity goes to the traction motors that are large electric motors mounted on the driving axles and truck frames.

This is, of course, greatly simplified, and how this all occurs is significantly more complex. Individual components have evolved substantially from the early diesel era to today. Alternators have replaced generators, AC traction motors have replaced DC motors, and advanced computer-controlled devices such as inverters have fine-tuned control for improved tractive effort and adhesion.

You don't need to be an electrical engineer to understand how these systems work. We'll try to stick with the basic concepts; full explanations of the technology involved fill entire books for each component.

Generators and alternators

Into the 1960s, locomotives relied on generators that produce direct-current (DC) electricity. The engine crankshaft turns an armature (electromagnet) within the fixed field coils ("stator," made of large copper windings, which create a stationary magnetic field) inside the generator that creates electricity. The power output of a locomotive is dependent upon the size and capacity of the generator to produce sufficient electrical

An Electro-Motive Division worker winds tape around the armature of a new model D87 DC traction motor in 1983. It will then be heat-treated before installation in the traction motor case. *EMD*

It takes several miles of wire to build a diesel-electric locomotive, even with the coming of modular electrical and electronic components. Here EMD wireman John Stalmack strings a high-voltage cabinet board for a new SD45-2 in 1973. *EMD*

The main generator is attached to one end of the engine; in this case, a Westinghouse 480-D main generator driven by a Baldwin 608NA (non-turbocharged) in-line eight-cylinder engine. A smaller auxiliary generator is mounted on top of the main generator. The caged shield at the end covers the belt that runs from the main shaft to power the auxiliary generator. *Baldwin; collection of H.L. Broadbelt*

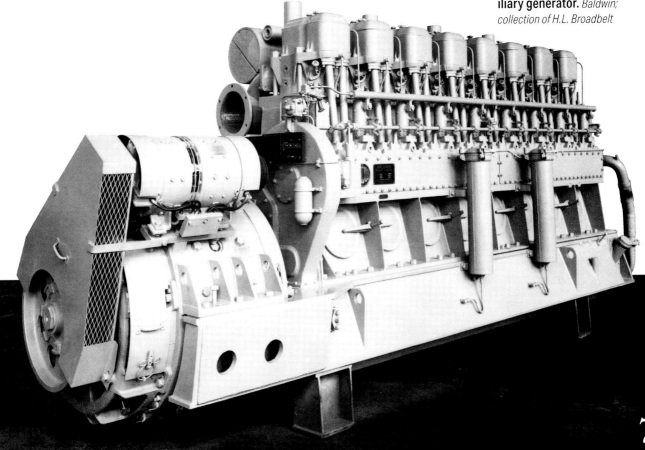

power. Generators on locomotives can put out 600 to 1,200 volts, furnishing 1,000 amps or more to traction motors.

Generators on locomotives are large (weighing 8 tons or more), complex, and expensive. The generator (along with the crankshaft) is one of a locomotive's most-valuable components. They are rugged, but they can experience failure. A main generator failure is an expensive problem. On an older locomotive it can lead to retirement. The worst-case scenario for a generator is a flashover, caused by a sudden overload, high-voltage grounding, short-circuit, or insulation failure not checked by a fuse or circuit breaker. The sudden release of high-voltage, high-current electricity and resulting powerful arcing can melt insulation, damage internal components, and cause an engine-room fire.

As engine and locomotive size grew, combined with more-robust traction motors that could handle increased power, generators also had to increase in power output and size. By the 1960s, generators

The new AR-15 alternator in 1980 was used in EMD's 50-series locomotives. The device was rated at 1,350 volts and had a continuous rating of 4,680 amps for traction motors. Alternators allowed traction motors to be permanently wired in parallel, with no need for transition shunting.
EMD

had grown to the point where it was getting difficult to fit the required generator inside the locomotive engine compartment of high-horsepower road switchers.

The solution was to switch to an alternator, which produces alternating current, or AC, instead of a generator. Alternators are smaller for the amount of power produced compared to a generator, as they are mechanically simpler in design. Alternators produce three-phase AC (there are three separate windings in the alternator, offset 120 degrees from each other), which then requires conversion to DC before it can be used by the traction motors. This is done with banks of high-capacity silicon diodes.

Alco was the first to do this, with its 3,000-hp Century 630 in 1965. EMD followed with its AR-10 alternator in its high-horsepower GP/SD40 locomotives later that year and GE with its GTA-11AC alternator for U30 locomotives the following year. Initially, alternators were only used for high-horsepower diesels, but eventually AC transmission became standard for all models.

It's important to understand that "AC transmission" using a generator is not the same as "AC traction," which means AC traction motors. That change would come in the 1990s (more on this in a moment).

Generating electricity for traction motors is more complex than simply having the diesel engine turn the generator/alternator. At any given throttle setting, the engine will turn at a set speed in rpms. However, the power requirements of the traction motors will vary, and the generator/alternator power output must vary to match what's needed. The output is determined by both the speed of the armature rotation and the amount of excitation current being fed to its field windings. The traction motors provide back-electromotive force (back-emf or counter-emf) to aid this excitation control.

This is a fancy way of saying that the engine (and its governor) and generator/

A bank of solid-state silicon diodes are installed on a new EMD AR-10 alternator in 1965. The diodes convert AC generated by the alternator to DC for use by the traction motors. *EMD*

Traction motor components

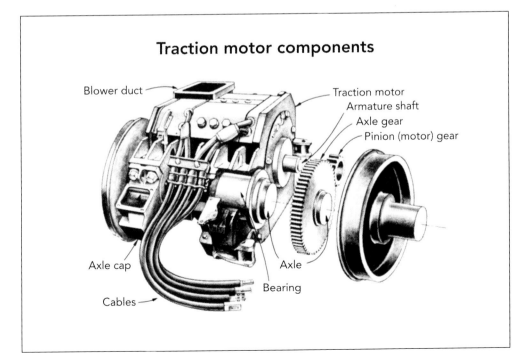

Blower duct

Traction motor
Armature shaft
Axle gear
Pinion (motor) gear

Axle cap

Axle

Cables

Bearing

The main components of a traction motor are shown here. The near side of the motor rides on the axle; the far side (nose) rests on the truck frame. Gears are shown open for clarity, but are enclosed in a gearbox when installed. *Kalmbach Media*

GEAR RATIOS

Part of what makes diesel locomotives so versatile is that they can be set up with gear ratios that provide either higher low-speed tractive effort with lower maximum speed, or lower tractive effort but higher maximum speed (gears can also be changed out on existing locomotives). This means the same locomotive type can be suitable for drag-freight service on heavy grades, high-speed service on the prairies, or a compromise of the two.

A diesel locomotive's gear ratio is stated simply by the number of teeth on the large gear on the axle and the number of teeth on the smaller pinion gear on the traction motor. For example, on EMD's F and GP diesels, which had 40-inch wheels in their Blomberg trucks, available gear ratios included 65:12 (45 mph maximum), 62:15 (65 mph), 61:16 (70 mph), 60:17 (77 mph), 59:18 (80 mph), 58:19 (89 mph), and 56:21 (102 mph). The Lackawanna, for example, had some F units with 65:12 gearing for mountain helper service; Santa Fe had high-speed Fs with 56:21 gearing in passenger service.

For any given locomotive type, the total number of teeth between the two gears is the same. Changing a locomotive's gear ratio involves swapping out both the pinion and axle gears.

A replacement EMD traction motor rests on the floor at a Louisville & Nashville shop in the 1950s. When the axle at rear is installed in the hole/bearings (near side of the traction motor), the large axle gear will mesh with the small pinion gear on the motor. *William A. Akin*

alternator adjust to the demands being put on it by the traction motors. You can hear this when listening to a train at full throttle, for example, as it transitions from level running to the start of a grade. The throttle setting and engine rpms remain the same, but you can hear the engine begin to work harder as the traction motors increase their current draw and the alternator/generator subjects the engine to more turning resistance.

The traction-power circuitry is a high-voltage (600-1,200 volts) system. It, and each of the locomotive's other electrical circuits, is a closed system — there's no common ground connection through the locomotive frame as with an automobile. There's a ground relay connected to the locomotive frame. If it senses a current leak from any power circuit, the relay will trip and take the generator/alternator off line to avoid potential damage.

Locomotives have a separate small aux-iliary generator, belt-driven by the engine drive shaft, as part of its low-voltage (64-72V) system. This charges the locomotive batteries and, while the engine is running, powers lighting, locomotive control (throttle, etc.), radios, and other devices, and on some locomotives serves to start the engine.

Traction motors

Traction motors are heavy (6,000 to 7,200 pounds) high-voltage electric motors mounted on the axle and truck frame (details on that in Chapter 5). All traction motors on diesel-electric locomotives into the 1980s were DC powered, with AC technology emerging since that time. Four-axle locomotives have all axles powered. Early six-axle passenger diesels (and some six-axle freight diesels designed for light rail) had four powered axles, with most modern six-axle freight locomotives having all axles powered.

The drawing on page 73 shows the basic components of a traction motor. The motor

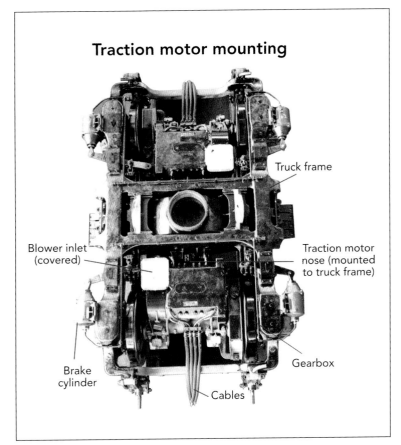

Traction motor mounting

Truck frame

Blower inlet (covered)

Traction motor nose (mounted to truck frame)

Brake cylinder

Gearbox

Cables

One side of the traction motor is mounted to the axle; the other (nose) is mounted to the truck frame. The gears are enclosed in a gearbox. This is an EMD "Blomberg" B truck. *EMD*

has a small (pinion) gear that meshes with a large gear on the axle inside of one wheel. The drawing shows this as open, but as the top view of a truck shows (above), the gears are enclosed in a gearbox with grease to keep out contaminants and keep it running smoothly. A series of four cables at one end are connected to power leads from the locomotive.

Traction motors produce high torque and power, placing a lot of stress on their internal components. They operate at high temperatures and are air-cooled via an opening at the top of the motor. A blower on the locomotive forces air to the opening through ductwork. Without this cooling, motors will overheat.

The DC traction motor is a four-pole, series-wound device, with a typical maximum speed of about 2,500 rpm. Depending upon a locomotive's intended use,

The General Electric model 752 is one of the most commonly installed DC traction motors of all time. This 5GE752ES motor was built in 1959, and will be used in a new U25B.
General Electric

the gear ratio between the pinion and axle gears (see "Gear ratios" on page 74) can be adjusted to provide maximum tractive effort at low speed or to allow a higher maximum speed with less starting tractive effort. Based on the gear ratio used, the locomotive's maximum locomotive speed reflects the need to keep the motor's armature under its maximum rotational speed. This can range from 35 mph for a switcher to 70 mph for a freight locomotive to over 100 mph for a passenger unit. Exceeding the maximum rated speed can damage or destroy the traction motor, even on a locomotive that's not under power.

Inside the motor is a rotating shaft which carries the armature, which has a laminated steel core wound with insulated copper coils connected to a commutator. The armature passes through stationary carbon brushes that contact the commutator; electricity from the generator goes to the brushes and commutator, creating a magnetic field that causes rotation.

A DC traction motor is powerful with excellent high-torque characteristics, but a disadvantage is that its moving parts (commutator and brushes) experience wear and are subject to failure and damage from heat generated during operation. The higher the current load, the hotter the motor becomes and the shorter time it can operate without damage. The motor's "thermal limit" is the temperature that will begin to cause damage.

All DC motors have a continuous rating (in amperes) at which they can operate constantly without damage, plus "short-time ratings," the amount of time they can operate at specific higher amperage levels. The higher the amperage, the shorter the allowed time. These ratings are directly tied to a motor's thermal limit or capacity — the ability of that particular motor design to handle high temperatures. An ammeter on the engineer's control panel shows the amperage being used, with a label showing the continuous rating and indicating short-time ratings at various current levels.

Reversing a locomotive with DC traction motors is done by reversing the flow of current through the field windings. This is controlled by the reversing lever on the engineer's control stand.

General Electric and Westinghouse were the prime suppliers of traction motors (and other electrical gear) to most diesel locomotive builders through the 1940s. Both supplied equipment for heavy electric locomotives starting in the early 1900s. Electro-Motive used GE and Westinghouse equipment through the late 1930s, but developed its own motors and equipment by 1940.

Notable early traction-motor models include the Westinghouse model 370, which earned a reputation for toughness and the ability to withstand overloading longer than other contemporary motors. It's larger than other motors, and was widely used by Baldwin and Fairbanks-Morse locomotives, which both had reputations for locomotives with good low-speed lugging abilities. Westinghouse discontinued its line of locomotive electrical equipment in the early 1950s.

General Electric's model 752 traction motor first appeared in the 1940s, and with upgrades continued serving until the coming of AC motors. Alco notably used these motors, as did Baldwin and FM after Westinghouse left the business. The 752 was GE's choice for many of its electric locomotives and then for its own line of diesel-electric road switchers upon the introduction of its Universal line in 1959. This motor earned a good reputation for performance and reliability.

Electro-Motive developed its own design for traction motors (and other electrical gear) in the late 1930s to avoid dependence on outside companies. Its D-series traction motors have been continually upgraded, starting with the D7 model in the E3 in 1939 and progressing through the D90 of the SD70 series. The EMD motors, although capable, did not enjoy quite the same reputation for toughness as GE and Westinghouse designs, although modern versions were greatly improved.

Improvements in the GE and EMD designs largely hinged on improved, more-efficient insulation materials that allowed using more copper in the motor's armature coil. The result was increased short-time ratings and improved power output. These upgrades continued with the introduction of higher-horsepower locomotives that allowed longer and heavier trains.

Transition

As the amperage load on traction motors rises, voltage drops (and vice versa). To improve efficiency (and avoid commutator damage) on DC-transmission road locomotives, the wiring from the generator to the motors was changed in four steps ("transitions") to suit the current draw and improve efficiency. The rough equivalent of transition is a tractor-trailer starting in low gear or downshifting to climb a grade, but shifting to high gear when going 65 mph on a level freeway.

From high current draw to low, there were four transition steps:

1. Series-parallel: The Nos. 1 and 4 traction motors were connected in series, as were Nos. 2 and 3. This was for motors drawing the highest current (such as starting or on a heavy grade).

2. Series-parallel shunt: Same as 1, but the fields of each motor are shunted by resistors.

3. Parallel: All four traction motors are connected in parallel.

4. Parallel shunt: Same as 3, but with the motor fields shunted by resistors. Used for low-current-draw operation.

Through the 1940s, transition was made manually by the engineer, using a lever on the control stand. The ammeter (see page 79) on these locomotives has markings that show when transition should be made. Automatic transition became an option by the late-1940s and was standard by the mid-1950s, with relays triggering the steps automatically (most older locomotives were retrofitted with automatic transition). In the 1960s, as locomotives moved to AC transmission, the need for transition disappeared, and traction motors were always wired in parallel.

Switchers, because they had a smaller speed range, generally had no transition or just two transition steps. Electro-Motive's SW1, for example, originally had all four motors always connected in series; later versions added series-parallel.

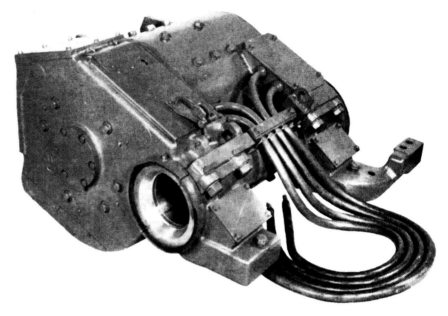

Baldwin and Fairbanks-Morse were noted for using the Westinghouse 370 traction motor, which was larger and had heavier insulation and materials compared to other motors of the 1940s and 1950s. It had an excellent reputation for durability and lugging ability. *Westinghouse*

Workers change out a traction motor on an EMD locomotive on a drop table at Southern Railway's Alexandria, Va., shops in 1947. The job takes about two hours. *Sol Libsohn*

AC traction motors

The advent of the AC traction motor is the biggest revolution in modern locomotive design. Their main advantages are durability and dramatically increased wheel-to-rail adhesion. An AC traction motor uses the alternating flow of AC power instead of a physical commutator to provide rotational motion. Eliminating the commutator and brushes makes AC motors lighter, more reliable, more powerful, less prone to damage from water, and nearly impossible to burn out.

The advantages of AC motors had long been known, and they had been used on some electric locomotives. However, the challenge was in controlling their speed effectively. The advent of improved microprocessors finally made AC traction feasible. After much experimentation, culminating with EMD's SD60MAC demonstrator locomotives starting in 1991, Burlington Northern ordered 350 of the first production AC locomotives — the SD70MAC — in 1993. General Electric began building its AC-traction AC4400CW the same year.

AC = increased adhesion

Gaining as much adhesion as possible for each powered wheel has been a challenge since the days of steam locomotive. Even with clean, dry wheels and rail, many forces intercede to make getting a good grip challenging. Each locomotive wheel contacts the rail on a tiny area: the size of roughly a dime. Uneven weight loading among wheels and axles can cause slipping, as can too much power being applied. External materials — moisture or any foreign materials on the rails such as grass and leaves — are especially troublesome.

Early diesels typically achieved adhesion of around 20% depending upon rail conditions, and the coming of microprocessor controls (which could quickly detect and correct wheel slippage by automatically reducing power and applying sand) for modern DC locomotives, together with improved truck designs, bumped adhesion to about 30% on dry rail.

New AC locomotives dramatically improved upon that, achieving adhesion factors in the mid- to high-30% range in all

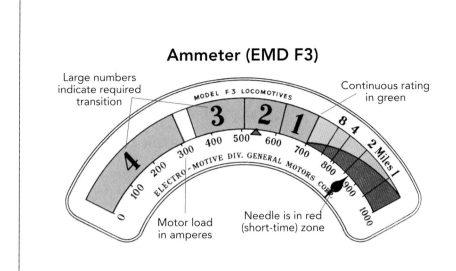

Ammeter (EMD F3)

Large numbers indicate required transition

Continuous rating in green

MODEL F3 LOCOMOTIVES

ELECTRO-MOTIVE DIV. GENERAL MOTORS CORP.

Motor load in amperes

Needle is in red (short-time) zone

Ammeters show an engineer how much power is being used by each traction motor, an especially vital piece of information with DC motors. On this EMD F3 ammeter example, the needle is approaching 900 amps — well into the short-time rating — and the gauge shows the locomotive can operate less than two miles at this level without sustaining damage. The engineer would have shifted to transition 1 (series-parallel) long before the needle reached this point. *EMD*

conditions, and up to 45% in ideal conditions. The net effect is significant enough that railroads are finding one AC locomotive can replace two DC locomotives of the same horsepower rating in many situations.

This improvement is largely because with an AC motor, a microprocessor controls the specific motor speed. Unlike a DC motor

that will spin rapidly if it loses traction, the AC motor is trying to turn only slightly faster than its actual speed, so if it slips, the effect is minimal. Also, any slip is detected immediately by analysis of the motor and corrected.

Another benefit of AC traction motors is greatly increased dynamic braking control,

The simpler design of AC traction motors, like this GE GEB13, allows finer control and makes them nearly impossible to burn out from overloading. They also provide much greater dynamic brake control. *Greg McDonnell*

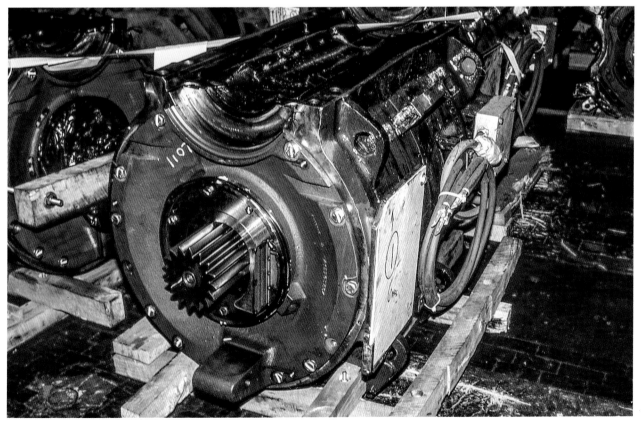

Modern AC locomotives, like this Union Pacific GE ES44AC, use inverters to "chop" AC power for traction motors. On GE/Wabtec locomotives, the inverters are in the cabinet directly behind the cab on the conductor's (left) side.
Jeff Wilson

with effective braking possible even under 1 mph (more on that in Chapter 7).

AC traction control

On an AC-traction diesel, an alternator generates AC power, but rectifiers are still used to convert it to DC. Microprocessor-controlled devices called inverters take the resulting DC current and convert it to three-phase AC for the traction motors. It's a complex process, with part of the challenge dealing with electricity that varies in voltage as well as frequency (unlike your AC house current that is always at 60 Hertz).

After conversion to AC, the inverters "chop" it to regulate the power output and rotational speed, turning the power on and off rapidly (up to 500 times per second). These inverters have evolved significantly as well, from early gate turn-off thyristors to gate bipolar transistors by the early 2000s. Again, you don't need to know the specific electronics — just understand that the new devices are smaller, require less energy to operate, and are easier to keep cool.

On its early AC diesels, EMD used one inverter rack per truck, while GE used one for each axle/motor on its AC4400CW;

EMD began offering six inverters as an option on its SD70ACe, and six became standard on the current SD70ACe-T4.

Even at an added cost of $500,000 to $1 million more per locomotive, AC locomotives grew in popularity among Class I railroads as they saw the increased traction benefits. Many railroads initially purchased AC locomotives strictly for heavy-haul applications, but then the trend moved toward AC for all uses, and no new DC-traction locomotives have been built since 2012. In addition, some railroads (notably Norfolk Southern) in the early 2010s began converting many older DC-traction locomotives to AC traction, contracting with GE and other builders.

Locomotive control

The traction-control system is operated by the engineer using the throttle. The throttle handle on the control stand has eight power settings ("notches") plus idle; early GE road diesels had 16 settings, and most switchers had "swipe" throttles without notches to make it easier to achieve quick acceleration and deceleration while moving cars in a yard. Chapter 8 goes into details of engineer's controls and cab designs.

These AC traction inverters are ready for installation at GE's manufacturing facility. They're installed in cabinets inside or along the hood of the locomotive. *Greg McDonnell*

Computer displays are standard on modern locomotives like this EMD SD70ACe. They provide real-time information including speed, throttle settings, end-of-train device, brake pressure, tractive effort, and the status of various components and systems. The control stand at left includes the automatic and independent brake handles at far left, and from top down in the middle are the dynamic brake lever, throttle lever, and a slot for the reverser handle (removed). *Jim Wrinn*

Throttles on some early diesels were pneumatically controlled, but since then all have been controlled electrically (they're part of a locomotive's low-voltage system). In each throttle notch, a different combination of four solenoids is energized in a drum contactor. These electrical signals are sent to the engine governor, which then regulates the flow of fuel and thus the engine speed.

One of the chief advantages of diesel locomotives over steam is the ability to connect multiple locomotives electrically and control them from a single point. This is known as multiple-unit (m.u.) control. All road locomotives are now so equipped, as were most early road switchers. Early

An m.u. cable is plugged into the socket mounted on the front platform of a Santa Fe FP45. The socket cover lid is hinged and sprung. The cable transmits electrical information between locomotives, allowing them to be operated together. *Jeff Wilson*

cab units often had m.u. connections only on the rear of A units (and both ends of B units), but most railroads eventually added connections to A-unit noses for added flexibility. Although switchers typically did not have m.u. connections, some did.

The m.u. socket or receptacle location varies; it's usually at deck level just above the anticlimber on road switchers, and sometimes on an elevated stand on earlier diesels. The socket has a hinged protective cover that flips down when not in use. On cab-unit noses, the connection is usually behind a small hatch on either side of the upper headlight. The socket could also be on an external fixture mounted to the nose if added later.

A heavy jumper cable connects receptacles of mating engines. The cable ends and sockets have standardized connections. Since the late 1940s, most railroads have used 27-pin connectors, although early diesels sometimes varied by manufacturer and railroad.

There were exceptions, but by the late 1950s it became common to see locomotives from multiple manufacturers set up to operate together, with railroads modifying cables and electrical gear to allow compati-

bility. An exception was Baldwin locomotives that used air-activated throttles.

Along with electrical m.u. connections, there are several air hoses on the pilot on either side of the coupler along with the main (train line) hose. These hoses (three, four, or five hoses per side depending upon the brake system used by the locomotive) control the independent (locomotive) brakes, equalize the train-line brakes (more on that in Chapter 7), and control the sanders.

When connected, all locomotives in a consist will respond to (and mimic) the controls in the lead locomotive. Thus if the lead locomotive is in notch 6, the trailing units will also go into notch 6, resulting in whatever engine speed their fuel rack settings call for. Any locomotive in a consist can be isolated if needed or desired.

In placing locomotives in consists, railroads generally try to match locomotives by characteristic, although you will sometimes see locomotives of widely varying horsepower and type grouped together. More critical is having the same or similar gearing, both to ensure a similar speed response among locomotives and to avoid damaging the traction motors of a low-gear-

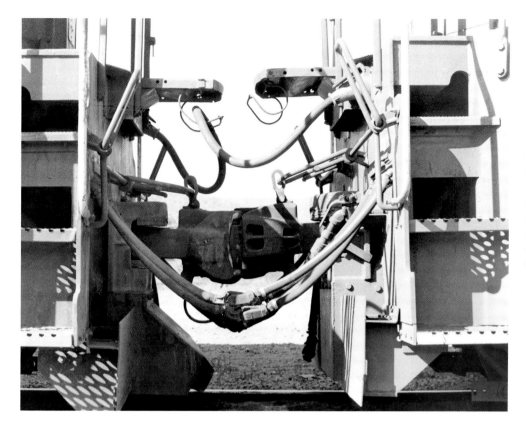

From top: Drop steps have been lowered on each locomotive to enable safe passage between units. The heavy electrical m.u. cable is connected to a socket on each locomotive; note how the drop steps have hangers to help support the cable. At bottom, hoses are connected to provide air connections for the automatic and independent brakes.
Trains collection

Batteries

Enough battery power must be available to start the diesel engine — 400 amps or more — and it can take several seconds for the engine to start. The batteries are also responsible for furnishing low-voltage power for lighting, controls, and other devices. A set of locomotive batteries is typically 32 cells (eight four-cell units or a similar combination) and can weigh 3,000 pounds or more. The batteries are charged by the auxiliary generator. The locomotive's low-voltage system is 64 or 72 volts.

Battery location varies by locomotive. On road switchers, the batteries are typically located in a compartment above the frame and walkway, often next to the cab, with access by ventilated side panels (often with small horizontal-slit louvers). Locomotives in service for substantial time will often show some white corrosion at these locations. On cab units, the batteries were typically below the floor with access

Multiple-unit sockets on cab units were often located behind hinged doors on either side of the upper headlight.
Trains collection

ratio engine caused to rotate too fast when coupled to a high-speed engine.

High-speed wheel slip of one locomotive in a consist is serious, and can damage track as well as locomotive components (as the photo on page 84 shows). This can be caused by pairing locomotives of widely varying gear ratios or tractive effort, where a heavier locomotive maintains traction while the lighter locomotive slips.

Locomotives of varying types and power and different manufacturers can be operated in multiple with each other, provided their m.u. connections are compatible. Here a six-axle Reading EMD SD45 (3,600 hp) leads a four-axle EMD GP30 (2,250 hp) and six-axle Alco Century 630 (3,000 hp) at Allentown, Pa., in 1968. *Allan H. Roberts; J. David Ingles collection*

through the engine room (making access difficult) or under the frame next to the fuel tank, with access via side panels.

Electrical cabinets and controls

Between high- and low-voltage systems, locomotives have a lot of wiring — six miles of it or more — along with hundreds of switches, sensors, connectors, circuit breakers, and relays. Since the 1980s, this also includes multiple computer and microprocessor systems. Keeping track of these circuits, and organizing them

neatly, is essential for troubleshooting.

Wires and cables for electrical systems are bundled and routed through conduits or behind panels to centralized control cabinets that are generally located at the wall between the engine room and cab. The cabinets include switches, relays, meters, fuses, circuit breakers, and other control and monitoring devices. The engineer's stand and control panel includes control switches for headlights, classification lights, and cab interior/gauge lights, as well as indicator lamps for wheel slip, ground-relay, low oil, and over-

High-speed wheel slip can happen if locomotives of different gear ratios are operated together, or if a lighter-weight locomotive slips while heavier locomotives maintain traction. This can obviously damage motors, wheels, and rail. Here a Pan Am (former Boston & Maine) GP40 is losing its footing in 2016. *Robert A. Stein*

Electrical cabinets are usually located on the wall separating the cab from the engine room. This is the high-voltage cabinet of a new EMD GP30 in 1961. Although the wiring is greatly simplified compared to earlier diesels, compartmentalized electrical and electronics modules are still a few years away, as evidenced by the hard-wired switches, relays, fuses, breakers, and large bundles of wires. *EMD*

heating. The panel also has an ammeter to show current draw of traction motors.

Early diesels were hard-wired among components. Centralizing electrical components allowed more-efficient construction and also made repairs easier. As electrical devices improved in reliability and shrunk in size, builders moved to modular components to enable easier change-out of parts. This moved to full solid-state electronic modules by the 1970s, where each module could feature redundant circuitry and, if needed, be removed and replaced in a matter of minutes. This modular design was a major highlighted feature of EMD's Dash-2 line (1972) and GE's Dash-7 locomotives (1976).

Head-end power

Steam generators were used to supply heat as well as power lighting and air conditioning for most passenger cars into the 1970s (see Chapter 9). By the 1960s, some commuter agencies had turned to electrical power supplied by the locomotive to do this; some early diesel streamliners with dedicated consists also used variations of these systems, which became known as

head-end power (HEP). It took until the 1970s for HEP to see large-scale adaptation for intercity trains, marked by delivery of Amtrak's first new Amfleet cars in 1975.

The HEP system used by Amtrak (others are similar, but variations exist) uses a 480-volt, 60-hertz, three-phase AC line — supplied by a locomotive or separate generator car — that runs the length of each car. The end of the locomotive (and each HEP-equipped car) has four connectors, one for each of four parallel circuits. Capacity varies, ranging from 500 kW up to 1,200 kW on some modern locomotives.

On a locomotive, the HEP system consists of either an alternator powered by a separate small diesel engine or by a connection to the locomotive engine's main driveshaft (called "shaft-driven HEP"). Constant speed is required for the alternator (to keep the frequency steady at 60 Hz), so locomotives with shaft-driven HEP are set up so that the engine runs at a constant speed when HEP is being used. (See "F40PH shaft-driven HEP" on page 90.) On locomotives with a separate HEP engine-alternator set, the unit is usually at the rear of the locomotive. Its location can

By the 1970s, modular wiring was becoming standard — see the middle row of replaceable modules. The EMD worker is checking wiring connections before the electrical cabinet is installed in a Santa Fe SD40-2 in 1981. *EMD*

STARTING AN ENGINE

Starting a locomotive engine is more complex than starting an automobile. It requires a lot of power because of the engine's size and high compression ratio. On generator-equipped locomotives, an additional winding in the generator allows it to also function as a motor. To start the engine, the fuel pump and other systems are turned on. Electricity from the locomotive's batteries are applied to the generator windings, which turns the generator, which turns the engine crankshaft, which starts the engine.

This doesn't work with alternators, so either a separate DC motor is used or the auxiliary generator is used, with a DC exciter. Another option on some locomotives is an air starter, which uses an air-turbine motor (with its own air reservoir) to turn the shaft to start the engine.

Into the 1980s it was common to allow engines to idle at many times when a locomotive wasn't working, especially in cold weather where there's danger of the water system freezing. Modern locomotives have auto-start/auto-stop functions that, when engaged, will automatically turn an engine on and off as needed.

be spotted by a separate exhaust stack above it on the roof.

On any given train, only one locomotive's generator provides power. This is because of the nature of constant-frequency three-phase AC, and the challenge of matching the frequency among multiple generators. This is unlike old steam-generator systems, where multiple locomotives' steam generators would combine to supply the train system.

The first locomotive to use shaft-driven HEP was General Electric's U34CH in 1970, built for New Jersey Department of Transportation commuter service (operated by Erie Lackawanna). The U34CH was a U36C with an HEP alternator; the "H" meant HEP-equipped, with 3,400 hp available for traction.

Amtrak's first HEP engines were cowl-design GE P30CH locomotives that arrived in 1974. They used pairs of small alternators powered by Detroit Diesel engines to supply electricity (750 kW total capacity).

It was the EMD F40PH, however, that became Amtrak's first primary locomotive. Amtrak's first new locomotives — the short-lived EMD SDP40Fs — were delivered with twin steam generators, but had been built to allow room for separate engine-alternator units. The F40PHs, which began arriving in 1976, originally had shaft-driven

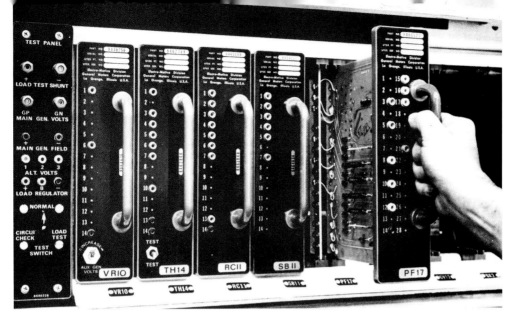

Electro-Motive's Dash-2 line introduced electrical cabinets with rows of modules for many locomotive control systems. They are easily removed and replaced. *EMD*

The General Electric U34CH, designed for push-pull commuter service, was the first locomotive with shaft-driven head-end power (HEP). Built for New Jersey DOT (operated by Erie Lackawanna), the first were delivered in 1970. They had high-speed (103-mph) gearing. *General Electric*

HEP systems, but many later versions had separate units (and some were rebuilt with separate engine-alternator sets), initially at 500 kW, later at 800 kW.

On modern AC-traction locomotives, microprocessors allow more-efficient HEP methods. Siemens Charger locomotives, for example, use a static inverter from the main engine to provide HEP at a consistent frequency (660 or 1,000 kW). They also have dynamic brakes that can route power to the HEP and auxiliary electrical system.

Microprocessors and computers

The coming of microprocessor control in the 1980s signified the start of the third generation of diesel locomotives. The first production locomotives with onboard computers were EMD's GP60/SD60 line in 1984 and GE's Dash 8 locomotives in 1985. The computing power in these first locomotives, although revolutionary at the time, is rather simple by today's standards. Microprocessors analyzed and corrected wheel slipping, which increased adhesion,

F40PH SHAFT-DRIVEN HEP

This description of how HEP works with a constant-speed engine, using EMD's F40PH as an example, is from "The Little Locomotive that Did," by Sean Graham-White and Lester Weil, published in the December 1999 issue of Trains.

In normal mode, to provide constant HEP, the prime mover is constantly running at full speed (893 rpm). The throttle in the cab does not change engine rpm, but increases or decreases the amount of current from the main generator to the traction motors. As engine rpms are constant, there's no change in sound as an F40PH in this mode accelerates or decelerates. If a train must lay over or remain in a station for an extended period, the HEP controls can be disconnected in "standby" mode. Engine rpms are reduced to 720, and the main generator supplies electrical current to the train. The throttle will not supply power to the traction motors in "standby." In "off" mode, no electricity is available for the train. The engine idles at 325 rpm, or 260 rpm for better fuel efficiency, and the throttle will operate the engine in conventional manner.

Only one locomotive can supply HEP to the train, so in a multiple-unit consist, the above only applies to the locomotive supplying HEP, and the power from that locomotive for traction will be reduced (up to 750 hp at peak HEP current draw). Other locomotives in the consist will have their full horsepower available for traction, with engines responding to throttle commands and varying in speed. — *Sean Graham-White and Lester Weil*

and a microprocessor replaced relays and switches for many engine-control functions, allowing faster engine response and more-efficient operation. These were also the first diesel-electric locomotives to have desk-style control stands, with display screens eventually providing readouts on the front panel. Those, and panels on the electrical cabinet, provide real-time information to operating crews on any problems or issues. They also allow maintenance workers to see a record of past problems, making it easier to diagnose and fix any issues.

The coming of AC traction required substantially more computing power, as explained earlier, and the introduction of positive train control (PTC) in the late 2010s — which tracks train locations and movements to avoid collisions — required even more. Emissions control is also dependent upon microprocessors to adjust settings and functions, as is the engine itself (governor, fuel injection). A new Tier 4-compliant AC locomotive with PTC has more than 200 onboard sensors and a total of about 15 million lines of code to track and operate its necessary functions.

This is reflected in the cab, which now has multiple displays that monitor functions (speed, throttle and brake settings, routes, signals and restrictions, engine performance, tractive effort), system availability, and efficiency. Computers also record performance and spot problems and potential problems that may require attention and maintenance. (See Chapter 8 for examples of cab displays.)

This has significantly changed operations. For example, let's say an engine is overheating. On an older (non-microprocessor) locomotive, a thermostat would trigger an alarm (bell) at a certain oil or water temperature, illuminate a warning light, and depending upon the specific problem, would shut down the engine or shift it to idle. With a modern locomotive, the system will analyze why temperature is rising in a certain system prior to it reaching critical temperature, diagnose the cause, pinpoint the location, and correct the

Top: General Electric's P30CH cowl-style diesels, delivered starting in 1975, were Amtrak's first electric head-end power (HEP) diesels. Two small diesel engine/generator sets were located in the rear compartment behind the grilles. The HEP cables are in four sockets — two atop and at each outer side of the pilot. *Gordon B. Mott; Louis A. Marre collection*

Left: Amtrak head-end power (HEP) circuits comprise four separate lines, with two cable bundles on the top of each side of the pilot. These F40PH locomotives are in Seattle in 1984. *Andy Sperandeo*

issue if possible (re-routing radiator flow, adjusting engine speed, etc.), in many cases correcting the problem before the engine shuts down. In cases where a shutdown is needed, the system will usually be able to provide a real-time diagnosis.

These systems increase a locomotive's efficiency and operations, but also add many areas where components and sensors can fail. High reliability of entire systems is necessary to make these innovations worthwhile, and a primary focus of locomotive builders is ensuring the reliability and durability of all of a locomotive's components.

All locomotives are now equipped with positive train control (PTC). The PTC computer (shown) is located inside the locomotive in a cabinet or other housing; it connects to the locomotive's software or, on pre-microprocessor locomotives, to sensors throughout the locomotive and a display screen in the cab.

Brian Solomon

Positive train control (PTC), which railroads began installing in 2008, was required on most lines by the end of 2020 (the original 2015 implementation deadline was extended). The goal of PTC is to avoid collisions and dangerous situations by monitoring train locations and speeds. It's an overlay to existing signaling and dispatching systems with the addition of GPS and other features, and has the ability to override engineers' controls, including applying brakes and stopping trains if PTC detects a dangerous situation.

The electronics required in each locomotive are extensive, and finding room for the equipment on existing locomotives was challenging. Along with display screens in the locomotive cab, other equipment includes a control unit/module, power supplies, and multiple antennas. System manufacturers include Alstom (Incremental Train Control System, or ITCS) and Wabtec (Positive Train Control Interoperable Electronic Train Management System, or I-ETMS). On locomotives with full-width noses, the equipment could go in the nose; on other locomotives, room was sometimes created in the cab itself, or above the cab behind the number boards.

On older (pre-microprocessor-era) locomotives, installing PTC takes more time (and is expensive) because it requires hard wiring the PTC to sensors and controls throughout the locomotive (to the engine control system, brake system, speed sensors, and others).

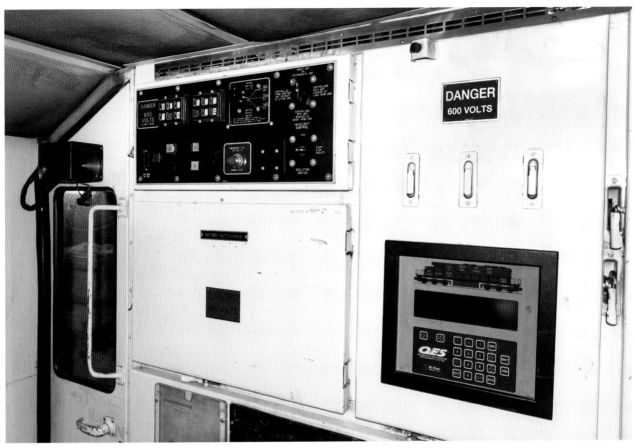

The electrical cabinet on this Morrison-Knudsen MK50-3 in 2017 includes standard control switches and lights at upper left, with a Wabtec Q-Tron monitoring screen at right. Q-Tron is an add-on system for older locomotives that provides microprocessor-based monitoring and control of many onboard systems.
Chip Sherman

Computer displays on the engineer's console have been standard since the late 1980s. This is a Union Pacific GE AC4400 built in 2003. It also features optional desktop-style controllers. *Union Pacific*

CHAPTER 5

TRUCKS & WHEELS

Trucks and wheels must transfer power between the loco-motive wheels and frame, and do so while maintaining maximum adhesion and provid-ing a smooth ride. This Union Pacific EMD SD60M rides on HT-C six-wheel trucks, a high-adhesion design first used with EMD's Dash-2 line in 1972. It's marked by a vertical damper on the center axle. *Jeff Wilson*

There is more to trucks and wheels than just
supporting the locomotive and helping it roll

Supporting the weight of a diesel-electric locomotive while transmitting engine power and braking force between the wheels and frame presents a significant challenge, especially as trains have evolved to be heavier and faster and locomotives have become more powerful.

While other builders had moved exclusively to truck-based construction, Baldwin in the early 1940s continued dabbling with unpowered lead and trailing trucks with driving wheels mounted in long, rigid frames. Number 6000 is an experimental demonstrator with a 4-D+D-4 wheel arrangement reminiscent of steam construction. It led to Baldwin's Centipede production locomotives; they were not successful. *Baldwin*

Wheel and traction design and methods for a diesel-electric are much different than a steam locomotive, which has larger wheels with prominent rods and valve gear that are in continuous motion. The ultimate solution for diesel-electrics was a truck with axles powered by electric traction motors mounted to the axles and truck frames.

Transmitting the power of traction motors (Chapter 4) to the driving wheels and axles has been the subject of much experimentation, with specific variables including wheel size, wheel mounting, number of wheels/axles, springing/cushioning/suspension, mounting the traction motor, and securing trucks and wheel assemblies to the locomotive frame/body.

Much of this experimentation was accomplished in the early 1900s via early heavy electric locomotives, which also used traction motors. Running gear on early heavy electrics was designed much like steam locomotives, with large driving wheels (50" diameter or larger) on axles mounted along a long frame, with smaller unpowered wheels mounted in pilot and trailing trucks.

Locomotives placed on pairs of trucks, with truck-mounted motor/axle/wheel assemblies, were largely reserved for smaller power units, such as streetcars, interurbans, gas-electric motor cars (doodlebugs), and boxcab and steeple-cab switchers.

Electro-Motive installed variations of this four-wheel freight truck, known widely as the "Blomberg" truck for designer Martin Blomberg, on locomotives from 1939 through the 1980s. This is the original design used on the first FT freight locomotives of the early 1940s. This particular truck frame was cast by LFM under contract for EMD. *EMD*

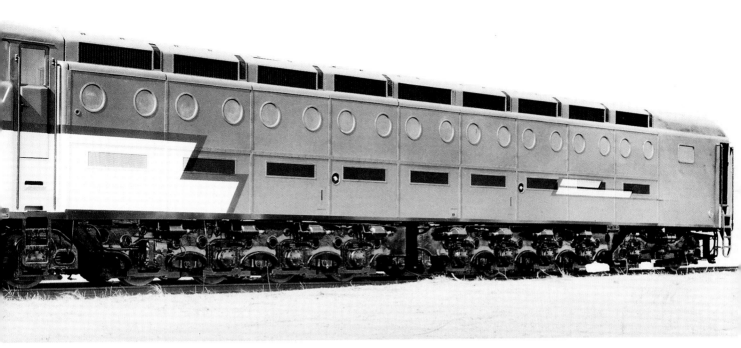

Locomotive truck (EMD B "Blomberg")

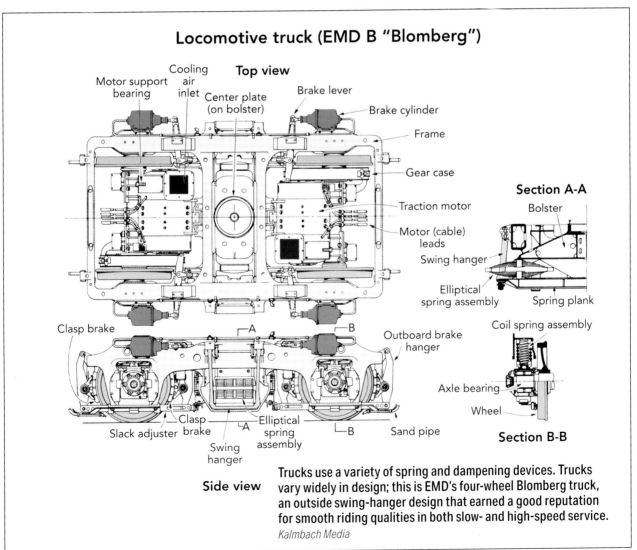

Top view

Motor support bearing

Cooling air inlet

Center plate (on bolster)

Brake lever

Brake cylinder

Frame

Gear case

Traction motor

Motor (cable) leads

Section A-A

Bolster

Swing hanger

Elliptical spring assembly

Spring plank

Clasp brake

Outboard brake hanger

Coil spring assembly

Axle bearing

Wheel

Section B-B

Clasp brake

Slack adjuster

Elliptical spring assembly

Swing hanger

Sand pipe

Side view

Trucks use a variety of spring and dampening devices. Trucks vary widely in design; this is EMD's four-wheel Blomberg truck, an outside swing-hanger design that earned a good reputation for smooth riding qualities in both slow- and high-speed service.
Kalmbach Media

Above left: The AAR Type B road truck was a common design used by Alco, Baldwin, and General Electric. It is a double-equalized design with a 9'-4" wheelbase (the heavy U-shaped beams are drop equalizers; the second is visible behind the front one) with both coil and leaf springs. *Jeff Wilson*

Above right: Late versions of EMD's Blomberg truck ("M") had a vertical damper on the right axle and a horizontal damper above the swing hanger. This is a BNSF (ex-Santa Fe) GP60M in 2006. *Jeff Wilson*

A few early diesel-electrics — notably some boxcabs and Baldwin's Centipede cab-unit locomotives — had driving wheels mounted in rigid frames. However, by the late 1930s, as diesel-electric switchers increased in number and size and diesel streamliners began to appear, designers shifted to locomotives riding on trucks.

Specific truck designs have varied widely by manufacturer and use (switching, passenger, or road freight). Trucks have evolved significantly over the years, with modifications and new designs aimed at improving ride quality and adhesion while minimizing wheel and rail wear. There's no way to cover every variation, so we'll start with a look at basic truck design and specific components, then examine several common or notable designs.

Designations

Truck types are identified and classified by the Association of American Railroads (AAR) according to their number of powered and unpowered axles, using letters and numbers. Letters refer to powered axles in a truck: A for one, B for two, C for three, and D for four. Unpowered axles are indicated by numbers. The most common trucks are C (six-wheel, three-axle truck with all axles powered), B (four-wheel, two-axle truck, both axles powered), and

A1A (six-wheel, three-axle truck with the two outboard axles powered and a center unpowered idler axle).

Trucks are further described by name and/or model designation and builder. Some of these common names are official and some are nicknames or were given by railfans and observers (see "What's in a name and who built them?" on page 97). Examples include EMD's Blomberg and Flexicoil, Alco's Blunt and Hi-Ad designs, GE's FB (floating bolster), and AAR Type A and Type B trucks.

Basic truck design and components

The basic components of a truck are shown in the drawing on page 95. It features an EMD B (GP) "Blomberg" truck, but others have similar components. Truck design involves many complex factors and engineering formulas regarding weight distribution, adhesion, motion forces, and shock forces. Designers aim for a smooth ride while minimizing overall truck weight, maximizing power to rails, and making maintenance (replacing brake shoes; turning/machining and replacing wheels; repairing and replacing traction motors) as easy as possible.

Truck frames are heavy cast steel, and with crossmembers the sideframes form

Switcher trucks featured lighter construction and a shorter wheelbase. The AAR Type A truck had primary suspension only, with an 8'-0" wheelbase. This early (1941) version has solid bearings (note the journal-box covers) instead of roller bearings. Note the cast-in GSC logo at right. *EMD*

WHAT'S IN A NAME, AND WHO BUILT THEM?

Modern locomotive trucks are usually given official designations by their builder — EMD's HTCR-6, for example — but this wasn't always the case, especially in the early diesel era. The result is that many common truck designs are best known by informal nicknames or simply by manufacturer and type.

So let's get a couple of things out of the way. Yes, most of us know that EMD's popular four- and six-wheel trucks of the 1930s through the 1980s were not officially named "Blomberg" trucks. But if you say "Blomberg truck" to almost any railfan or modeler, they will know exactly what you're talking about (even if they don't know that the name comes from their inventor, Martin Blomberg), and it's much simpler than saying "six-wheel Electro-Motive passenger truck" as the specification drawings stated. So Blomberg is entirely appropriate, and it is used freely throughout this book (and in most publications and websites).

The common four-wheel switcher and road trucks long built by General Steel Castings (GSC) under their Commonwealth brand (the company acquired Commonwealth around 1930) have long been known as AAR Type A and Type B trucks. However, although the switcher version was adopted as a recommended practice by the AAR in 1947 (per the 1950-1952 edition of the *Locomotive Cyclopedia*), the AAR never distinguished them as Type A or B: for example, the A was labeled "diesel locomotive switching truck." The Type A and B reference is much simpler and has become widely known enough to be perfectly acceptable. These are just a few examples … the list goes on with many others, but you get the idea.

Trucks were most often built by third-party manufacturers such as GSC, Adirondack, Rockwell (Locomotive Finishing Materials, or LFM), Atchison Casting, and Dofasco. These companies built trucks to their own standard designs as well as doing contract work for locomotive manufacturers. For example, GSC, which was co-owned by Alco, Baldwin, and American Steel Foundries, supplied trucks to all major builders, including Alco and Baldwin competitor EMD — you'll see many Blomberg trucks complete with GSC (see page 100) and LFM (page 94) logos, even though it was a proprietary design of EMD. Also, many trucks in GSC's line carried the "Commonwealth" name, but no single design was *the* Commonwealth truck.

The bottom line: Don't get hung up on semantics. Look at details to identify specific trucks, compare them to photos and drawings, and if you're modeling, compare models to prototype photos for accuracy.

a basic box that keeps all of the truck
components in alignment. The bolster is a
heavy horizontal crosswise member that
supports the locomotive frame in the middle
in a circular depression called a center plate.
The center plate holds the kingpin of the
locomotive frame's bolster, transferring all of
the forces between the locomotive and trucks.

Wheels are cast steel, mounted on
cylindrical axles. The axles are supported
on each end in either a journal box with
solid bearings (some early diesels, especially
switchers) or roller bearings (all modern
diesels and most road diesels from the 1940s
onward). These are held in the sideframes.
Powered axles have a gear located inside
one wheel with teeth that match a gear
on the traction motor (see Chapter 4);
the gears are enclosed in a gearbox. Most
freight locomotives use 40- or 42-inch-
diameter wheels, but some early passenger
locomotives used 36-inch wheels.

Springs (coil and leaf), snubbers, and
dampers (struts and shock absorbers) of
various types work together to cushion
the ride and distribute loads. The wheels
themselves, along with axles, roller-bearing
adapters, and the part of the traction
motor supported by the axle are "unsprung
weight." This means they take the full shock
of rolling motion, such as hitting rail joints
and frogs at crossings and turnouts.

A truck's "primary suspension" is the
spring system at the first point of contact
between the unsprung weight and the truck
frame, usually comprising multiple coil springs
atop the roller-bearing adapters, atop which
the sideframe rides. Depending upon the
specific truck design, these springs may be
visible or hidden in a pocket behind the frame.

The "secondary suspension" includes
a number of cushioning devices to control
motion. The bolster can be part of the truck
frame or it can float on the truck frame,
with each end supported by springs (usually
elliptic — also called leaf — style).

These springs rest on a spring plank, a
crosswise member below and parallel to
the bolster. On a swing-hanger truck, such
as the EMD Blomberg in the drawing, the
bolster, springs, and spring plank form a
cradle, which is supported on each side by
swing hangers. This keeps weight equalized
and smooths the ride by allowing limited
lateral movement while keeping components
cushioned and aligned, especially on
curves and on rough track. Some trucks are
plankless, with the bolster resting on pads on
the sideframes.

On a drop-equalizer truck, like the
Type B road truck, an equalizer — a heavy
frame member connecting adjoining axles,
usually a stretched U-shape — serves to
distribute the weight evenly between axles.

"Equalization" refers to distributing weight evenly among all wheels in contact with the rail as the individual wheels follow irregularities (ups and downs) on the track. On trucks without separate equalizers, the sideframe itself acts as an equalizer.

In addition to springs, many trucks use snubbers (shock absorbers or dampers) to control and cushion either vertical or lateral motion. These can be rubber cylinders combined with coil springs, or hydraulic or friction cylinders that look much like an automobile shock absorber. These compress to allow motion and provide cushioning, but are designed to return to their original position without repeated swaying or rocking, as can happen when only coil springs are used. As with springs, depending upon specific truck design, snubbers can be visible outside the frame or hidden behind other components.

The traction motor is supported by the axle on one side (on a pair of bearings) and a cross member of the frame on the other (nose) side, cushioned by a rubber-steel nose block. The motor cable connections are on the outboard end of four-axle trucks. Six-wheel trucks vary, as we'll see in a bit, with some modern trucks having all motors facing the same direction.

Each sideframe holds one, two, or three brake cylinders, which are connected via an air line to the locomotive's brake system. The piston on each cylinder, through a system of levers, controls the clasp brakes (and brake shoes), which contact the wheel treads. Depending upon truck design, there are one or two shoes per wheel. The tension can be adjusted with the slack adjuster. A chain from the locomotive's brake wheel is visible on many older trucks across the front of the frame, connected to the end of the piston on the brake cylinder. These often have a channel or tubular guide to keep the chain aligned.

Electro-Motive developed its Flexicoil four-wheel truck as an option for switchers. It allows higher speeds and a better ride than an AAR Type A truck, but is lighter and shorter than a Blomberg B. This one is on an SW1500 switcher in 2016.
Cody Grivno

Fairbanks-Morse developed its own version of the AAR Type B road truck for introduction of its C-Line cab units in 1950. It's a single-equalized truck with both leaf and coil springs. It can be identified by the curved bottom of the drop equalizer.
Fairbanks-Morse

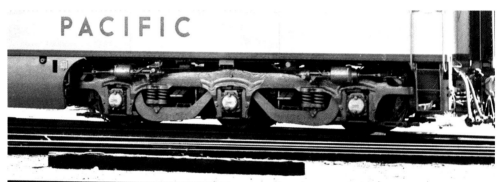

The EMD six-wheel Blomberg, used on passenger E units, is an A1A design (unpowered center idler axle) with swing hangers and 36" wheels. It had a reputation for smooth riding characteristics. This one was cast by GSC. *EMD*

The drop-equalizer A1A truck used on Alco PAs had a longer wheelbase (by 17") and larger (42") wheels compared to the EMD truck. It was also known for its smooth ride. *Union Pacific*

The kingpin of a locomotive (or the traction pin on modern bolsterless trucks) isn't fastened mechanically to the truck—gravity holds it in place in the center plate. To keep trucks from separating from the frame (or from over-rotating) in a derailment or accident, they are connected to the frame by safety chains or hooks, which are usually hidden from view under the frame.

Trucks vary by intended use. Switchers generally ride on lightweight, short-wheelbase trucks with primary suspension only, and they're designed for slow speeds. Freight trucks have longer wheelbases with primary and secondary springing and suspension. Passenger trucks are designed for high speeds, with additional springing/cushioning; many early versions were A1A designs with center idler axles, designed to provide a smooth ride at high speed.

Here's a look at several truck designs, starting with switcher trucks and moving to early road trucks and then modern hi-adhesion and steerable designs.

Switcher trucks

AAR type A — This four-wheel design was developed in the mid-1930s by Martin Blomberg, who later became better known for developing freight and passenger trucks at Electro-Motive. The design was widely used on switching locomotives from all manufacturers (the design was adopted as an AAR recommended practice in 1947). It was built by General Steel Castings, which had acquired Commonwealth in 1930.

The Type A is a short-wheelbase (8 feet even) truck using 40-inch wheels, with a simplified suspension. It has primary springing only, with a pair of equalizers on

SOLID-BEARING AND ROLLER-BEARING JOURNALS

Like freight cars, diesel locomotives have been built with both solid-bearing (often incorrectly called "friction bearing") and roller-bearing journals.

Solid-bearing journals have a babbitt-covered brass bearing that rides atop the axle end. This is enclosed in a journal box, which includes a cotton pad or clump of cotton fibers (called "waste") impregnated with oil to ensure that the bearing stays lubricated. A hinged lid on the journal box allows access for inspection and lubrication. They required constant maintenance to refill the journals; failing to do so would cause a dry bearing, which could ultimately lead to overheating (a "hotbox") and, if not discovered quickly, a fire and axle failure.

Roller-bearing journals are sealed packages that support the axle ends with multiple conical-shaped steel rollers. Along with greatly reducing rolling resistance, they are virtually maintenance free, usually able to go hundreds of thousands of miles before requiring relubrication or replacement.

Locomotives were faster to shift from solid- to roller-bearing journals than freight cars. Most road locomotives from the early 1940s onward were equipped with roller bearings. Switchers commonly had solid bearings, which wasn't as critical with their slow-speed operations (and they were usually stationed in yards near servicing facilities and received more regular attention), but they shifted to roller-bearing trucks by the late 1950s.

each side (the lower member is a long U shape that wraps toward the journal at each end). This makes the truck lightweight and economical, but it is suitable only for slow-speed operation in yards or on branch lines. It rides roughly at higher speeds, and wasn't meant to operate above 30 or 35 mph.

The design was used through the 1960s. Early versions usually had solid bearings, with roller bearings common by the late 1950s.

Blunt — This Alco design was also an 8'-0" wheelbase truck with 40-inch wheels, and it was named for its designer, James G. Blunt. Alco used it on its early (HH, S1, S2) switchers; like the Type A, it was a lightweight truck designed for slow-speed operation. It has distinctive equalizers compared to the Type A. The early version has coil springs visible above the equalizers just inboard of each wheel; later versions had bolster castings that covered the springs. Alco discontinued the Blunt and began using Type A trucks when it upgraded its switchers to the S3 and S4 in 1949.

EMD Flexicoil B — EMD developed the four-wheel Flexicoil truck following the design elements of the six-axle version (see page 105), adding a coil-spring secondary suspension for a smoother ride. It was intended as a lightweight 8'-0" wheelbase option on EMD's later switching locomotives (SW1000, SW1200, SW1500), allowing them to be operated in road service at higher speeds (up to 60 mph).

Early four-wheel road trucks

EMD Blomberg B — Although never designated as such by Electro-Motive, this four-wheel (9'-0" wheelbase) design became widely known for its designer, Martin Blomberg. It was first used on the pioneering FT road-freight diesel in 1939. The truck is an outside swing-hanger design (a feature heavily favored by Blomberg), which allowed lateral movement while providing a smooth ride and good adhesion even at high speeds. The B freight truck was based on Blomberg's earlier design for a six-wheel A1A passenger truck (also widely known as a "Blomberg" truck), but with

Top: Variations of the General Steel Castings A1A truck were used on passenger loco-motives by Baldwin and Alco. This Baldwin version from 1945 has 40" wheels and big Westinghouse model 370F traction motors on the outboard axles. *Baldwin; collection of H.F. Broadbelt*

Right: Alco's early A1A trucks on its RSC freight locomotives had a noticeably shorter wheelbase (11'-0") than passenger A1A trucks or various freight C trucks. This is a Union Pacific RSC2; it has GE 752 traction motors on the outboard axles. *Alco*

some key differences: mainly that the B truck used 40-inch wheels compared to the 36-inch wheels of the passenger trucks.

The Blomberg B became the most-used truck of the first- and second-generation eras, mainly because EMD built more diesels than any other builder. Along with F units, EMD used it on its popular GP line of road switchers. This basic design remained in production more than 50 years, through EMD's last four-axle diesels (GP60s in 1994), albeit with numerous upgrades, detail changes, and design tweaks.

The introduction of EMD's Dash-2 line in 1972 saw the move to the Blomberg M (modified) design, with a single brake cylinder and clasp brakes located only on outboard wheels, and the addition of a vertical strut over one axle. However, since trucks were among the most commonly rebuilt and re-used locomotive components,

it wasn't uncommon for earlier versions to appear under more-modern locomotives.

AAR type B — This double-equalized four-wheel truck is a stretched design of the type A, with a longer (9'-4") wheelbase, and is designed for higher-speed road service. A longer (9'-10" wheelbase) version was also built into the early 1950s for trucks using Westinghouse traction motors, which were bigger than GE motors. The Type B has both primary and secondary springing, with coil springs visible at the outboard gaps between the equalizers and a leaf spring in the middle, with a prominent drop equalizer.

Early versions first appeared in the 1930s, notably under EMD passenger demonstrators and power units of streamliners. The design became common in the 1940s starting with Alco's RS1 (and later FA-, RS-, and Century-series locomotives) as well as four-axle freight

locomotives from Baldwin, FM (early road locomotives), and General Electric. The Type B became the second most-common four-wheel road truck, with updated versions used into the 1970s. The Type B was a capable, cost-effective, and long-lasting truck, but had a reputation for rough riding — especially at higher speeds — compared to EMD's Blomberg.

Fairbanks-Morse developed its own single-equalized version (the "C-Line" truck), which it used on its road locomotives after 1949. It can be identified by the shallow curve on the drop equalizer.

Six-wheel A1A passenger trucks

EMD Blomberg A1A — Designed by Martin Blomberg, this distinctive design uses three axles to better spread the weight of EMD's double-engine passenger E units, with traction motors on the outboard axles and the center axle unpowered. Its long (14'-1") wheelbase and outside-swing hanger design (swing hangers between axles, two per side) allowed lateral movement with stability, giving the truck a reputation for smooth riding. These trucks used 36-inch wheels, which were lighter and provided a lower center of gravity compared to the 40" wheels of freight trucks. Another innovation was making the bolster hollow, allowing it to serve as the duct for traction-motor cooling air.

The truck was first used on the EA and E1 in 1937. It would be revised and modified over the years, but it remained in production until the last E9 was built in 1964.

GSC single drop-equalized A1A — Alco took a similar approach with its DL series of twin-engine passenger diesels and later single-engine PAs, placing them on GSC A1A trucks that used drop equalizers. This truck had a longer wheelbase

Six-wheel C-C Alco freight locomotives rode on Tri-mount trucks, which had two additional bearing surfaces (not visible from the side; see the FM truck below). The cables to each axle end are for wheel-slip controls. This is an RSD12 built in 1961. *G.W. Hockaday*

Fairbanks-Morse developed its own freight C truck. It has a single drop equalizer with struts combined with the spring packages on either side of the center axle. They were a tri-mount design — the kingpin is to the left of the center traction motor, with two bearing plates at angles to the right. *Fairbanks-Morse*

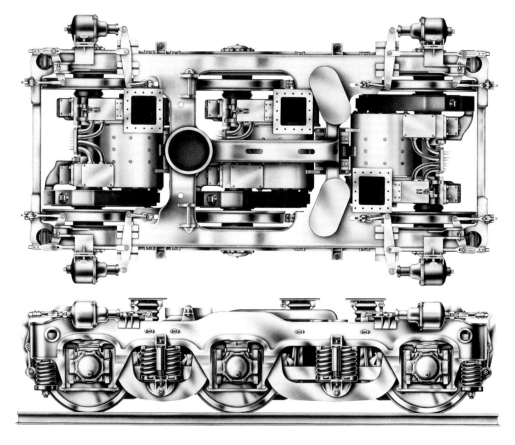

(15'-6") than the EMD A1A, with larger wheels (42-inch diameter), and was known as a smooth-riding truck. Fairbanks-Morse and Baldwin passenger locomotives also used a similar design, with some FM Erie-Built locomotives receiving fabricated (instead of cast) versions of the truck.

Early six-wheel freight trucks

Early road freight diesels were mostly four-axle, B-B designs. The first six-

General Electric used a version of the GSC Tri-mount truck on its early six-axle freight locomotives through the late 1960s. This Burlington U25C was built in 1965. *Louis A. Marre*

The EMD Flexicoil was the first C truck to have equal axle spacing, allowed by stretching the wheelbase about a foot longer than the GSC drop-equalizer design. It was used from the early 1950s through 1972; this one, on a demonstrator SD45 in 1966, has low-mounted brake cylinders. *EMD*

axle diesels were designed to better spread locomotive weight over additional axles, making them suitable for use on the lightweight rail of branch lines and secondary tracks. These used A1A trucks with center idler axles.

A problem was that these took a third of the locomotive's weight off of the driving wheels. This wasn't an issue with high-speed passenger locomotives, but was problematic for freight trains hauling heavy loads at low speeds. Manufacturers eventually realized that adding motors to the middle axles was worth the increased tractive effort, and six-axle locomotives

with all axles powered gained in popularity, especially for low-speed drag-freight service. However, six-axle C-C locomotives remained a niche product and wouldn't become popular for high-speed freight service until the late 1960s.

A1A designs — Freight A1A designs didn't follow passenger A1A designs. Shorter freight locomotive frames required shorter truck wheelbases, and the lower speeds didn't benefit from the better riding qualities of the longer truck. Alco's RSC truck was a GSC drop-equalizer design with an 11'-0" wheelbase with equal axle spacing (noticeably shorter than later C trucks

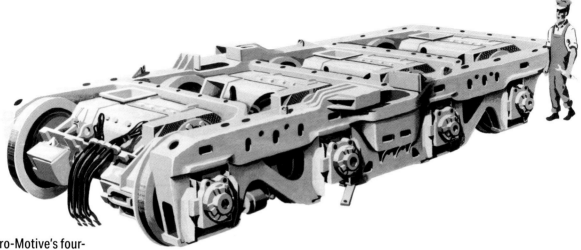

Electro-Motive's four-axle D truck, used on its twin-engine DD35 and DDA40X, is a variation on its Flexicoil design. The truck has a 20'-1½" wheelbase and weighs 37 tons. *EMD*

Alco's high-adhesion (Hi-Ad) four-wheel truck, introduced as an option on its Century locomotives, had a distinctive sideframe with the bolster end riding on a pair of coil springs. *Alco*

with all axles powered). Baldwin chose a cast non-drop-equalized design, also with equal spacing. As A1A freight designs fell out of favor, many Alco RSC diesels were retrucked with four-axle B trucks.

Early C designs — Alco was the first to offer a C-C freight diesel in the early 1940s, with the RSD1 (an RS1 with C trucks), and continued with the RSD4, 5, and later models starting in 1951. Other manufacturers followed: Baldwin's DRS6-6-1500 appeared in 1948 and EMD's SD7 and F-M's H16-66 in 1951.

The challenge of a C freight truck, compared to an A1A design, is providing room for the middle traction motor while keeping the overall wheelbase reasonably short. This is why early C trucks on Alco, Baldwin, and F-M diesels have unequal axle spacing: to allow room for traction motors, with two motors facing one direction and the third in the opposite direction.

GSC Tri-mount — Alco's double-equalized, rigid-bolster C truck (built by GSC) had a 12'-6" overall wheelbase (18 inches longer than its A1A truck), but axles unevenly spaced, at 6'-11" and 5'-7" — a very noticeable, distinctive detail. They were known as tri-mount trucks for their additional sliding bearing areas above each truck sideframe. This helped stabilize the ride and increase adhesion. Alco would use these through most Century-series models of the 1960s. Baldwin used versions of this truck on many of its later road switchers, and GE used a version on its six-axle U-series locomotives into the late 1960s. Fairbanks-Morse C trucks had a similar appearance, but were single-equalized, had a 13'-0" wheelbase (5'-9"/7'-3" spacing), and had vertical struts between axles. Early Baldwin C-C road switchers used cast trucks without drop equalizers. They had a 13'-0" wheelbase with 7'-3½" and 5'-8½" spacing.

EMD Flexicoil — For its SD7, which debuted in 1951, EMD designed a new truck. The Flexicoil stretched the wheelbase to 13'-7" to allow equal axle spacing. Modifying its highly successful Blomberg A1A passenger truck wasn't an option, because of the latter's lack of room for a middle traction motor and its use of smaller wheels (36-inch vs. 40-inch). Along with coil springs over the journals, the Flexicoil also supports the truck swing bolster on tall, large-diameter coil springs, allowing

Alco's six-axle Hi-Ad truck had a horizontal torsion bar in the middle, with vertical struts on the outboard side of each prominent coil spring. *Don Dover*

The short-wheelbase (11'-2") Dofasco high-adhesion truck was the first common bolsterless truck. It was first applied to MLW diesels and also used on Canadian C40-8M ("Draper Taper") cowl-body locomotives, including BC Rail No. 4613. *Cody Grivno*

REBUILDING AND RE-USE

Trucks are durable, and with regular maintenance will often outlast the locomotives under which they were delivered. Re-use of trucks from traded-in locomotives was regularly specified by many railroads, which is why it isn't uncommon to see second-generation locomotives atop older (albeit rebuilt) versions of first-generation trucks.

This also led to some odd matchups. Soo Line, for example, specified re-using the AAR type B trucks from traded-in Alco FA cab units under new EMD GP30s in the early 1960s, Chesapeake & Ohio received EMD SD18s riding on six-wheel tri-mount trucks from traded-in Alco RSD5s, and Seaboard Coast Line had BQ23-7, U18B, and other GE diesels riding on EMD Blomberg trucks.

The distinctive EMD HT-B four-wheel high-adhesion truck used larger wheels (42") and had a longer wheelbase than the Blomberg truck, meaning the two weren't interchangeable. It was not successful and was only used on a few experimental locomotives, including this Union Pacific GP40X.
Union Pacific

General Electric's floating-bolster three-axle truck (FB-3) was built by Adirondack (shown) and GSC. It has struts on the outboard axles and low-mounted brake cylinders. This one is under Southern Pacific U33C No. 8709.
Keith R. Tygum

The two-axle version of GE's floating-bolster truck (FB-2) was an option on its four-axle locomotives starting in 1972. It has a distinctive angled sideframe.
Louis A. Marre

the bolster to move laterally (and giving the truck its name). These trucks were EMD's standard until the introduction of the Dash-2 line in 1972, although the new HT-C truck was used on some locomotives starting in the mid-1960s. Variations mainly included brake cylinder and shoe location and number.

The four-axle (D) trucks used on EMD's DD35 and DDA40X locomotives were also a Flexicoil design.

High-adhesion designs

As horsepower increased — along with train sizes and speeds — by the 1960s, manufacturers were looking for ways to improve the factor of adhesion between wheels and rail. The result was a number of new truck designs from all major builders.

A main goal was to evenly balance the tractive forces among axles (and minimize slippage) during heavy acceleration. Picture the front wheels of a drag-race car lifting off the ground when rapidly accelerating because of the torque from its rear wheels: this is the same effect that can cause a lead axle of a truck to lose tractive force (even though it doesn't come off the rail). The new designs were meant to minimize these forces.

Alco Hi-Ad — Alco introduced two-axle (9'-4" wheelbase) and three-axle (13'-7") versions of this truck as options on its Century locomotive line starting in 1967. Alco's promotional materials touted these as "zero weight transfer" (ZWT) designs. Both can be identified by their prominent coil springs outside the frame.

Montreal Locomotive Works, which continued building Alco-design locomotives after Alco left the locomotive business in 1969, used a short-wheelbase (11'-2") three-axle truck produced by Dofasco on some of its M-series diesels. It was called variously the MLW Hi-Ad, ZWT-3, or simply the Dofasco truck (which can be confusing as Dofasco built trucks of many styles for several locomotive manufacturers). The design was the first common bolsterless truck, relying on a traction pin and connections from the body to the truck frames (see the section on steerable trucks for more details). The short wheelbase gives it a distinctive appearance.

EMD HT-C — A new six-wheel design replaced the Flexicoil on EMD's SD diesels, with modified secondary suspension springing. The trucks first appeared as standard under EMD's six-axle Dash-2

General Electric debuted its six-wheel Hi-Ad bolsterless truck with its Dash-9 series in the early 1990s. Some versions, like this one on a Union Pacific ES44AC (C45ACCTE to UP), have angled vertical struts on the outboard axles.
Jeff Wilson

109

Some older versions of GE's high-adhesion six-axle truck lack struts on outboard axles. Compare it to the UP diesel on page 109. This is BNSF Dash 9-44CW No. 5320 in 2007. *Jeff Wilson*

locomotives in 1972, although they had been tested as experimental designs on the SD45X and some other locomotives in the late 1960s. The trucks carry all three traction motors facing in the same direction. Visibly, they differ by having a damping strut over the center bearing on each side. The frames are similar to the earlier Flexicoils, but have three holes in the frame between axles (compared to two on Flexicoils). They were standard on EMD C-C diesels into the 1990s.

EMD HT-B — EMD introduced a new four-wheel truck in 1977, designed to improve response to wheel slip and to improve torque balance between axles. It used 42-inch wheels (instead of the 40-inch wheels on Blomberg trucks), had a longer wheelbase (9'-9¾"), and eliminated the swing hanger. The design was unsuccessful and was used on relatively few locomotives. It was expensive (using all new parts and technology) and its size meant it was not interchangeable on locomotives with the previous design.

EMD HTSC — Introduced in the 1990s, this is a non-steerable/non-radial version of the HTCR radial truck. Like the HTCR, it is bolsterless — see the HTCR entry for details. It remains an option for buyers who opt for non-radial trucks.

GE GSC and Adirondack FB-3 and FB-2 — General Electric in 1966 switched to a floating bolster design similar to the EMD Flexicoil. The new three-axle FB-3 had even axle spacing and eliminated the drop equalizers and uneven axle spacing of the earlier GSC truck. Versions of the FB-3 were made by both GSC and Adirondack (and their successors). Both were quite similar, with struts on the outboard axle ends, and they could have brake cylinders mounted in high or low positions. Later versions had a single strut on the center axle. Both had a 13'-7" wheelbase. These were used through GE's Dash-8 locomotives into the 1990s.

The two-axle (FB-2) version appeared in 1972 as an option to the AAR B truck. It's a 9'-0" wheelbase with a distinctively shaped

Electro-Motive was the first to offer a steerable truck ("radial" to EMD) as an option in the early 1990s. On EMD's HTCR design, the steering linkage is inside the truck frame. This one is on a Union Pacific SD70ACe. *Jeff Wilson*

The latest version of EMD's radial truck, the HTCR-6, has a fabricated frame, which is lighter than earlier cast versions. The two body/truck frame mounting pads are visible between lead/middle and middle/rear axles, and the horizontal steering linkage is visible below the sideframe. *Cody Grivno*

cast sideframe that angles downward from the wheels to the center, with the bolster above the middle of the sideframe. It was used on many GE locomotives through the end of four-axle production in the early 1990s.

GE/Wabtec Hi-Ad — GE's Dash 9 line in the early 1990s debuted the Hi-Ad truck, a bolsterless design (see the GE Hi-Ad steerable entry). The frame lines are straighter compared to the earlier FB-3, with some versions having angled struts on the outboard axle ends. The non-steerable Hi-Ad lacks the center angled linkage outside the frame that's found on GE's steerable truck. Variations of this truck are still used on current Wabtec locomotives that don't have steerable trucks.

Steerable (radial) trucks

A historical problem with six-wheel trucks is that their rigid design keeps all three axles parallel with each other. Together with the trucks' long wheelbase, this means that on curves, the center axle is the only one that follows the radial line (exact radius) of the track, with the leading and trailing axles at slight angles. The result is that these trucks on curves tend to "hunt," as flanges of the wheels on the lead axle hit the outer rail, shift, then repeat the process through curve, leading to a jarring back-and-forth motion. This is made worse the higher the speed and the sharper the curve.

Associated problems include increased wear to wheels and rails and lowered

The GE/Wabtec steerable truck has the linkage clearly visible on the outside of the truck frame, arching over the center axle bearing. This is a Canadian Pacific AC4400. *Cody Grivno*

This is the A1A truck used on the GE/Wabtec six-axle, four-motor locomotive, the ES44C4. It's designed as a lower-price option with the comparable pulling power of a DC-traction locomotive. *Chris Guss*

adhesion (traction) on curves, a problem especially critical on grades with curves, where the lowered adhesion results in measurably less available tractive effort.

The solution on modern locomotives is the steerable (also called "self-steering" or "radial") truck. On these, the center axle is rigidly mounted (but allowed to move laterally), but the outboard axles are allowed slight pivoting motion to angle toward the curve. Upon entering a curve, the lead axle senses the shift and turns slightly into the curve; linkage connected to the trailing axle causes it to simultaneously turn the opposite direction. This keeps all axles radial — matching the radius of the curve — hence the name. The result is a smoother ride, much-improved adhesion with more power to the rail (and less chance of wheel slip), and less wheel and rail wear. Although

many current locomotives have steerable trucks, some railroads have continued opting for standard trucks due to higher initial cost and increased maintenance.

EMD HTCR — EMD, which calls its version a radial truck, was the first to introduce the design, making it an option on its SD70 series in the early 1990s. Initial versions have cast frames; the latest version, the HTCR-6, has a lighter fabricated frame. Radial trucks became standard equipment on EMD's Tier 4 SD70ACe-T4 in 2015.

The HTCR is a bolsterless design. Instead of a traditional bolster, there are five contact points at each truck: The main one is the traction pin (which replaces the kingpin/bolster/center plate), which transmits acceleration and braking forces — but not locomotive weight — between the truck and frame. The frame/body weight is carried

Modern four-axle passenger locomotives have all moved to bolsterless, high-speed truck designs. This is a Siemens Charger (SC-44) on Via Rail Canada, built in 2021.
Stephen C. Host

by two contact points above each side of each truck, with springs (a firm steel/rubber combination) that support the body and allow for lateral movement and forces. These (nicknamed "elephant feet") appear as large round black objects atop the sideframes.

GE/Wabtec Hi-Ad Steerable — General Electric introduced its version, which it calls "steerable," on its Dash 9 series in the 1990s. The frame has a different appearance compared to its standard Hi-Ad truck (and the EMD HTCR), with a distinctive arched linkage above the center journal on each side. Like the non-steerable version, it is also a bolsterless design. Steerable trucks remain an option on current Wabtec locomotives; they have not been as popular as EMD's HTCR trucks.

Modern A1A, B1 trucks

Since the 2010s, both GE/Wabtec and EMD/Progress Rail have offered four-motor/six-axle versions of their standard AC-traction locomotives: Wabtec has the ET44C4; EMD the SD70ACeP4-T4. This is largely done to provide a lower-cost alternative to six-motor AC locomotives while providing about the same tractive effort as a C-C DC-traction locomotive.

Wabtec's trucks for these are A1A, with traction motors on the outboard axles and the center axle unpowered. The trucks can increase or decrease the weight applied to the center axle, increasing the weight on the powered axles when necessary.

EMD's design places the unpowered axle on the inboard (fuel tank) side of each truck, giving the SD70ACeP4-T4 a B1-1B designation.

Modern passenger

Four-wheel freight trucks ended production with the demise of the four-axle freight locomotive in the early 1990s — including the Blomberg design also used on F40PH passenger diesels. The new monocoque passenger locomotives that began appearing in the early 1990s (GE Genesis series, EMD F125, MPI MPXpress, and Siemens Charger) all use four-wheel trucks of distinctive high-speed, bolsterless designs. The first Genesis locomotives had trucks from the German company Krupp Verkehrstechnik, later part of Siemens Mobility.

CHAPTER 6

BODY DESIGN & LOCOMOTIVE TYPES

Advancing design and technology led to varied locomotive models

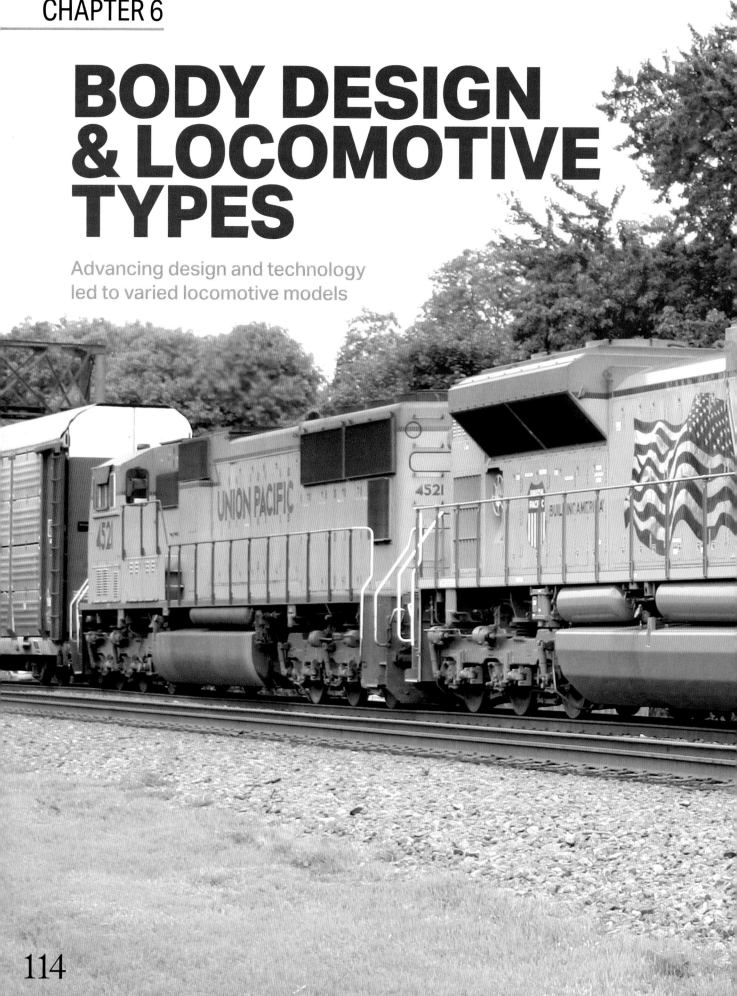

The road switcher became the dominant freight locomotive in the 1950s, with high-horsepower, six-axle, wide-nose versions becoming the norm by the 2000s. Here a Union Pacific SD70ACe and an older SD70M lead a train on Union Pacific in 2006. *Jeff Wilson*

Diesel locomotive body design has evolved significantly since the 1920s. Body styles, sizes, shapes, and overall features have been driven by several factors, including operator visibility and access to controls; space needed for the engine, generator, and other internal equipment; providing ample strength to carry the body and components; protecting gear from the elements; operator safety; intended use; and efficiency and cost of manufacture.

Since the dawn of the diesel era, manufacturers have built locomotives in four basic body styles: boxcabs, end-cab switchers, carbody or cab unit (streamlined) road locomotives, and hood-style road switchers (including cowl-body variations).

Regardless of body style, the first requisite in building a locomotive is a strong frame. A modern road locomotive weighs more than 210 tons; even switchers of the early diesel era often weighed 100 tons or more. Carrying the engine, generator, and other equipment requires a strong base of support that won't sag or experience twisting or bending when dealing with the torque and slack action of train forces, even after 30 or 40 years of service. Some early switchers and road locomotives used cast-steel frames. However, by the late 1930s most manufacturers had moved to fabricated frames, with H- or I-beams and steel plates and shapes welded together.

Early diesel bodies were initially quite utilitarian, not much more than a sheet-metal shell enclosing all the components. As more locomotives entered service, it was obvious that changes were needed to improve visibility, with the end-cab switcher appearing by the 1930s. Appearance became important with the introduction of streamliners in the early to mid-1930s, which led to similarly styled freight locomotives. And finally, form

The first diesel-electric switchers and road locomotives featured boxcab designs, like this Alco-GE-Ingersoll-Rand 60-ton, 300-hp switcher built for Central of New Jersey in 1925. Visibility, especially to the rear, was not good, nor was access to the engine and other interior components.

Trains collection

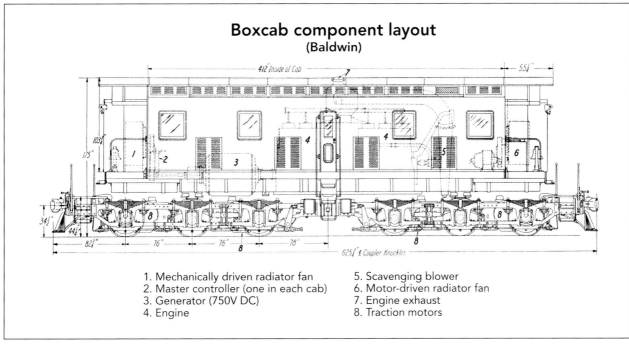

Boxcab component layout
(Baldwin)

1. Mechanically driven radiator fan
2. Master controller (one in each cab)
3. Generator (750V DC)
4. Engine
5. Scavenging blower
6. Motor-driven radiator fan
7. Engine exhaust
8. Traction motors

followed function as the road switcher became the dominant locomotive style by the 1950s. Compared to early diesels, crew visibility was improved and access to interior components was better, making locomotives easier to maintain.

Crew safety today is a key element of locomotive design, with modern locomotives having wide noses with collision posts and cab interiors designed for both safety and comfort. This certainly wasn't the case with early diesels. Room for the engineer and fireman

sometimes appeared to be an afterthought; some early streamliners (notably the *Zephyr* and other shovel-nosed designs) had engine components intruding into the cab area, with the engineer and fireman in dangerously low positions at the extreme front of the cab. It unfortunately took accidents involving early streamliners and other locomotives to push designers to move cabs upward and behind noses for safety.

Let's look at the basics of each body style and see how they evolved.

Baldwin's first diesel-electric was an A1A-A1A boxcab switcher (see the prototype photo on page 16). *Baldwin*

Among the first road diesels was Canadian National No. 9000, a two-unit set of 1,330-hp passenger locomotives from 1929. They were built by Canadian Westinghouse with Baldwin bodies. Beardmore V12 engines took up much of the interior. *Canadian National*

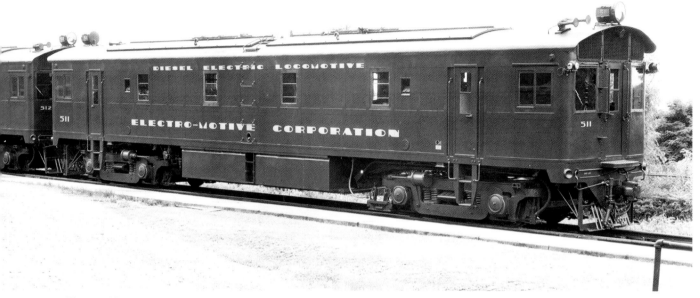

Electro-Motive experimental passenger boxcabs 511 and 512 were twin-engine (Winton 12-201A) 1,800-hp, four-axle locomotives that led to the company's streamlined E series cab units. *EMC*

Boxcabs

Boxcab locomotives — known as such since they resembled a boxcar with a cab — featured a squared-off body with a built-in cab on one or both ends. Their design was a carryover from the style of many earlier electric locomotives, including heavy road locomotives and low-speed switchers as well as interurban freight motors.

The first diesel-electric switchers of the 1920s, most commonly by the consortium of Alco/General Electric/Ingersoll-Rand (Alco-GE-IR), as well as subsequent switchers built by GE/IR, Baldwin, and Electro-Motive, were boxcab designs. They were relatively small, from 60 to 120 tons and 300-800 hp with one or two small diesel engines. They had cast frames and sheet-steel bodies with windows at the front and sides at the cab end(s), and many included a window or two along the body in various patterns to allow light into the engine room. Some had access doors on the sides and others on the front, and some had front platforms with side or corner steps.

Most of the interior was taken up by the engine and generator, and the fuel tank was usually placed inside the body as well. Those with single engines had the engine centered in the body, while twin-engine locomotives had the engines side-by-side (facing opposite directions) with a small walkway between them. The radiators were placed on the roof, with air reservoirs below the frame between the trucks.

The boxcab design was also used on the first road passenger diesels of 1929: a pair of locomotives built by Canadian Westinghouse with frames from Commonwealth and bodies by Baldwin, with Beardmore V12, 1,330-hp diesel engines, for Canadian National. Far from slow-speed switchers, these were designed for 70-mph operation on the *International Limited* from Montreal to Toronto. They were built with steam-style running gear, with unpowered lead and trailing trucks and large driving wheels in rigid frames.

Electro-Motive Corp. also used the boxcab style for its experimental twin-engine passenger locomotives of the mid-1930s, with examples delivered to Santa

Rock Island No. 772 is an EMD NW2, a 1,000-hp switcher built in 1949. It is typical of the thousands of end-cab switchers built from the 1930s through the 1970s. *Jeff Wilson collection*

Switcher components

1 — Horn
2 — Air compressor
3 — Auxiliary generator
4 — Aux. generator exciter
5 — Main generator
6 — Generator blower
7 — Generator exhaust stack

8 — Engine
9 — Exhaust manifold
10 — Exhaust stack
11 — Engine air intake filter
12 — Lube oil tank
13 — Balance shutters
14 — Number board

15 — Radiator shutters
16 — Coupler
17 — Trucks
18 — Main air reservoirs
19 — Fuel tank
20 — Battery box

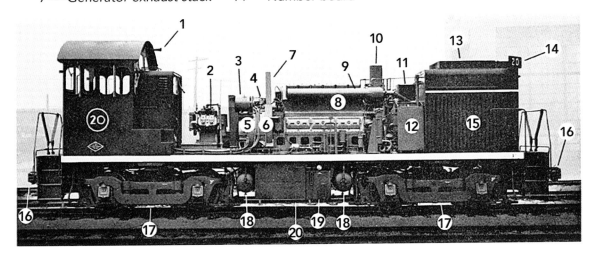

Component layout for end-cab switchers is similar to that of road switchers, but with a smaller, more-compact engine, generator, and other parts. This is a Lima-Hamilton switcher. *Lima-Hamilton*

Early diesel-powered streamliners were the precursors of later streamlined passenger locomotives. By the time this Union Pacific *City of Denver* train was built in 1936, power units were no longer articulated with their train sets, but still were styled to match the cars. *Union Pacific*

Streamlined passenger-service cab units were the first off-the-shelf road locomotives. Alco answered EMD's E unit series with its DL locomotives, including this twin-engine, 2,000-hp DL103b built in 1939 for the Rock Island. *Alco*

Fe and Baltimore & Ohio. The company revised the design, using what it learned from the boxcabs in developing its successful E unit series of streamlined carbody locomotives.

By the mid-1930s, boxcabs gave way to other designs. The boxcab design had several disadvantages. The locomotives had poor visibility to the rear—a critical factor for switching locomotives. Access to the engine, generator, and other internal components was difficult, especially if major repairs were needed. The blunt front end provided little safety in the event of accidents and collisions, especially for road locomotives.

End-cab switchers

As diesel-electrics began finding their niche as capable switching locomotives, manufacturers revised the body designs to improve visibility. In 1931, GE/IR built

seven custom 300-hp switchers for Bush Terminal (Brooklyn, N.Y.), featuring separate cabs. The cabs were full width, while the hoods were narrower, allowing for a walkway along each side. The design provided much better visibility than boxcab locomotives, and doors along the hood allowed engine and component access.

Alco, which had broken away from GE/IR to produce its own diesel-electrics, gets credit for the first off-the-shelf end-cab switcher in 1931. Other builders shortly followed, including Electro-Motive in 1935, Baldwin in 1936, and Fairbanks-Morse in 1944. Hood height varied by manufacturer based on the engine used, with some full-height and others short enough to allow windows on the cab wall above the hood. The end-cab design proved practical and economical to build, provided good visibility, allowed better component access,

This EMD F7 on a hoist shows how the side trusses were constructed, adding strength to the body so the frame could be lighter. The Alabama Great Southern (Southern Railway) locomotive is being lowered onto its trucks. The front kingpin is visible, just above and to the left of the worker's head. *EMD*

and proved popular among railroads.

Switcher frames were heavy, and although some early switchers had cast frames, manufacturers quickly switched to welded construction (more on those in the road switcher section). Components were arranged along the center of the frame, and although specific component location varied among models and manufacturers, the photo on page 119 shows a typical arrangement. Access doors along the side provided interior access, and for major work the entire hood could be lifted off by a hoist or crane.

Basic switcher design would remain relatively unchanged through the 1970s, when the number of classification yards

began dropping significantly. Railroads also began using older four-axle, low-horsepower road switchers in yards. The last conventional end-cab switchers (EMD MP15Ts) were built in 1987.

Carbody locomotives

The streamlined carbody or cab-unit style has its roots in the 1930s diesel-electric power units built for new streamlined passenger trains, starting with the Budd/Electro-Motive Corp. *Zephyr* (Chicago, Burlington & Quincy) and Pullman/EMC M-10000 (Union Pacific), both in 1934. The first streamliners had power cars initially articulated with their train sets, but later power units were built as separate

121

EMF F7 CUTAWAY VIEW

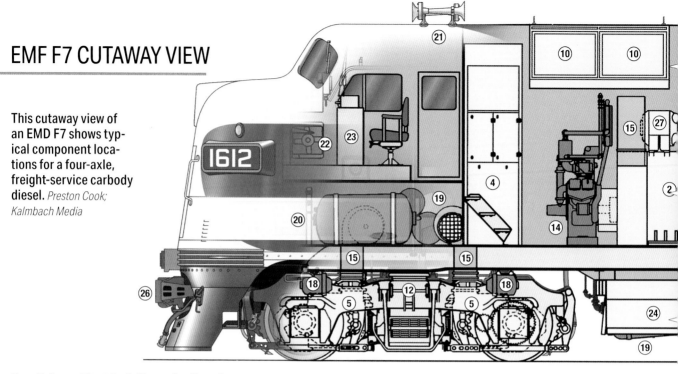

This cutaway view of an EMD F7 shows typical component locations for a four-axle, freight-service carbody diesel. *Preston Cook; Kalmbach Media*

Key: Yellow = Electrical; Blue = Cooling; Orange = Lube oil; Red = Fuel/exhaust; Light green = Blowers/fans; Dark green = Brake system

1. 16-cylinder 567B engine
2. Main generator
3. Companion alternator
4. Electrical cabinet
5. Traction motors
6. Radiator
7. Lube oil cooler
8. Radiator fans
9. Lube oil filter tank
10. Dynamic brake (optional)

11. Fuel tank
12. Blomberg B truck
13. Steam generator (optional)
14. Air compressor
15. Generator/traction motor blowers
16. Coolant tank
17. Roots blower
18. Brake cylinders
19. Air reservoirs
20. Sand boxes (on side walls)

21. Horns
22. Cab heater
23. Operator's controls
24. Battery compartment
25. Exhaust manifolds
26. Couplers
27. Auxiliary generator
28. Lube oil strainers

Fabricating carbody-style cabs (like this EMD FT in 1943) was more time-consuming than building a road switcher cab. After assembling the frame, sheet-metal had to be formed to complex curves over the framework, then welded, puttied, and shaped. *EMD*

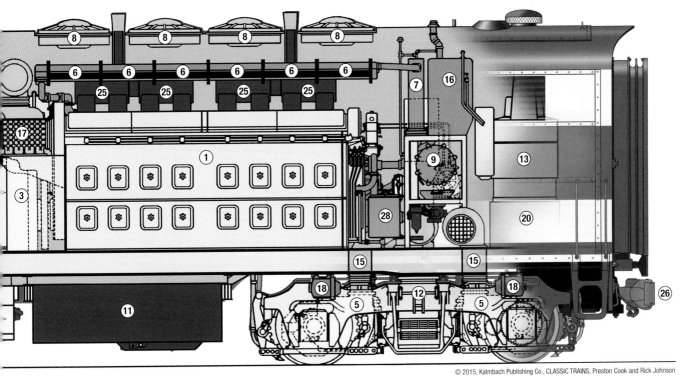

locomotives — but still designed to match specific trains.

In 1935, EMC built a couple of experimental twin-engine passenger locomotives that weren't designed for specific trains. The first experimental versions looked like boxcab designs, with blunt fronts. They had four-wheel trucks but were longer than earlier boxcabs to hold the two engines; commercial versions were sold to Baltimore & Ohio and Santa Fe.

These were redesigned with streamlined noses (with high cabs behind the nose) and six-wheel trucks, emerging as EMC's first E units in 1937. Electro-Motive followed with the first of its single-engine, four-axle freight F units — the FT — in 1939. Other manufacturers also introduced carbody diesels, including Alco with DL-series twin-engine passenger locomotives in 1939 and then single-engine passenger PAs and freight FAs after World War II, Baldwin with "babyface" and shark-nose cab units in freight and passenger versions, and Fairbanks-Morse with its Erie-Built and C-Line diesels.

Cab units were more than simple streamlined locomotives. An important design feature was that the sides were steel trusses — like bridges — attached to the sides of the underframe. These trusses added significant structural strength, allowing a thinner, lighter underframe. The body sides were metal panels (or a metal/plywood sandwich) held to the side trusses by batten strips, while the nose and front were sheet steel over posts. The nose and cab provided more protection for crews compared to boxcabs and most early streamliner power cars.

A wall at the rear of the cab held an electrical cabinet, with one or two doors opening to the engine room. The engine, generator, and main components were mounted along the center of the engine room, with narrow walkways on either side. Fans and dynamic brake housings were roof mounted. When steam generators were used, they were at the rear of the locomotive (more on those in Chapter 9).

The biggest issue with carbody locomotives was access to the engine, generator, and other major components. As the photo on page 126 shows, there wasn't much space in the engine room, and there were numerous ancillary devices, cables, and blower ducts in the way.

There was no external access through the sides of the body, as the truss structure was in the way (just a small access door or two). Major work required removing roof hatches, but even that was not ideal. This became more critical as locomotives aged and required more maintenance.

The design was also expensive to build. The truss sides and multiple curves of the streamlined noses were time-consuming to construct, adding to the expense.

Operationally, engineers praised cab units for their great visibility to the front, and for their tall cabs with their wide noses

E7 CUTAWAY VIEW

1. Engine no. 1 (12-567A)
2. Engine no. 2 (12-567A)
3. Main generators
4. Load regulators
5. Traction motors
6. Radiators (shown on engine no. 1 only)
7. Coolant tanks
8. Engine cooling fan
9. Lube oil filter tank
10. Steam generator water tank
11. Fuel oil tank
12. Truck (Blomberg A1A)
13. Steam generator
14. Air compressor
15. Traction motor blower
16. Lube oil cooler

17. Engine Roots blower
18. Brake cylinders
19. Air reservoirs
20. Bell
21. Horns
22. Operator's controls
23. Cab heater
24. Battery box
25. Exhaust manifold (shown on engine no. 2 only)
26. Couplers

Key
Yellow = electrical; Blue = water/cooling; Orange = lube oil system; Red = fuel/exhaust; Green = air brakes/fans

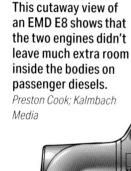

This cutaway view of an EMD E8 shows that the two engines didn't leave much extra room inside the bodies on passenger diesels.
Preston Cook; Kalmbach Media

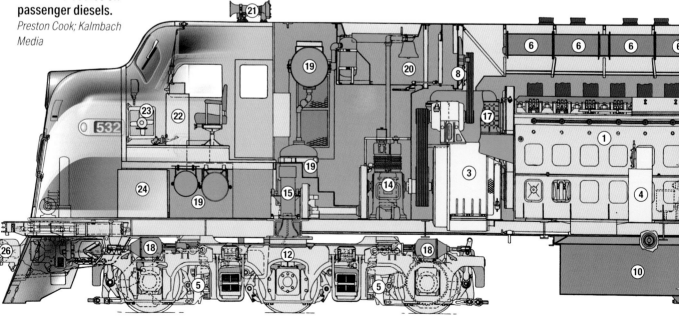

EMD'S BLUNDER: THE BL2

Not every locomotive design can be a success, and Electro-Motive — by far the most successful builder of the first half-century of diesel production — came up with a dud with the BL2. The BL2 is a convoluted design, with semi-streamlined styling that included notches along the sides of the body to allow for improved rearward visibility. It was intended for light-duty service; EMD promotional materials at the time described the BL2 as an F3 adapted for branchline service ("BL" for "branch line").

The BL2's structural design was that of an F unit, with truss sides and lighter underframe, and a lowered engine-room floor between the trucks. It was about seven feet longer than an F unit, and it required significant engineering modifications to rearrange many radiator, cooling, and engine accessories to fit the unique body. It was expensive and labor-intensive to produce, difficult to work on, and not popular with railroads. The demonstrator BL1 (with an air-actuated throttle and no multiple-unit capability) was released in September 1947; all production models had electric throttles and m.u. (hence BL2; the demonstrator was rebuilt to a BL2 as well). Only 59 were built, for nine owners, through May 1949. Even though the BL2 was unsuccessful, it did help iron out many bugs in developing the later GP7 (a conventional road switcher that would be extremely successful).

The semi-streamlined EMD BL2 was built with truss sides like an F unit but with tapered side walls to allow rear visibility. It was expensive to produce and did not sell well. *EMD*

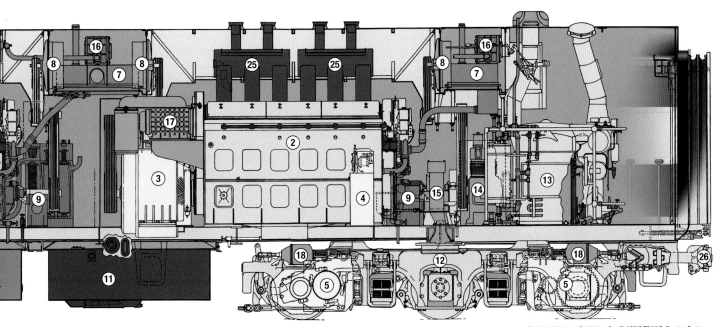

Carbody locomotives didn't provide a great deal of access space for working on the engine and other components. This is Santa Fe maintainer W.F. Leverenz checking on the 567 engine on a Santa Fe EMD FT in 1943. *Jack Delano, Library of Congress*

providing safety in collisions. Rearward visibility was another matter, however, as engineers had to lean out windows to see anything behind them. This was difficult at best and hazardous in many situations, especially at night and in poor weather. Cab units were obviously poor choices for local freights or any trains that did significant en route switching. These factors all led to the popularity of road switchers by the 1950s.

Cab-unit sales dropped significantly by the mid-1950s. The last traditional cab units were EMD dual-service (electric/diesel-electric) FL9s built for New Haven in 1960 and a few passenger E9s delivered to Union Pacific in 1964. Most of these early cab units were retired by the late 1970s.

The next streamlined diesels that appeared (from the late 1960s into the 1980s) were enclosed "cowl" body locomotives, but these were simply road switchers with added side sheathing — more on those in a bit.

Streamlined locomotives re-emerged with the introduction of GE's Genesis-series monocoque-body passenger diesels in the early 1990s. The P40DC is a 4,000-hp locomotive with a 103 mph top speed. *General Electric*

Monocoque streamlined diesels continue to dominate the passenger market. This Siemens ALC-42, delivered to Amtrak in 2022, is a 4,200-hp, AC-traction locomotive with 44" wheels and a blend of dynamic, regenerative, and electro-pneumatic braking.
David Lassen

The carbody design did not completely disappear, however, as a new generation of streamlined designs emerged for passenger locomotives in the 1990s. A directive and specifications from Amtrak, which was looking for new intercity locomotives, led to the design of General Electric's Genesis series locomotives in 1992. Models in this series included the P40DC, P32AC, and P42DC, and were built through 2001.

These are distinct from cowl locomotives in that they feature monocoque (unibody) construction, where the body shell and shape itself (with its framed corner posts and cross members) supports much of the load, allowing a lighter underframe and overall lighter weight. This makes them a modernized descendant of the original cab units of the early diesel era.

These locomotives have a lower profile for clearance. The lower center of gravity and streamlined nose and body help cut wind resistance and improve efficiency. Other manufacturers building monocoque streamlined units include MPI (MPXpress series, since 2003), EMD (F125, 2015), and Siemens (Charger series, ALC-42 and

Alco produced the first road switcher, the 1,000-hp RS1. It remained in production almost 20 years, from 1941 to 1960. These former Minneapolis & St. Louis RS1s are working for successor Chicago & North Western in the Twin Cities in 1967.
J. David Ingles

An advantage of the road switcher design was better access to the engine and other components compared to cab units. Hood doors open accordian-style. This is a new Southern Pacific EMD SD9 in 1954. *EMD*

others, 2017). The latest versions, operated by Amtrak and various commuter agencies, are Tier-4 compliant with AC traction and advanced microprocessor controls.

Road switchers

Alco is credited with creating the road switcher design with its RS1 of 1941. It was built at the request of the Rock Island (its

No. 748 was the first), which was looking for a switcher that could also be used at higher speeds in light road service. Alco took its S1 end-cab switcher, stretched the frame, added a short hood on the end of the cab, and placed it on longer-wheelbase road

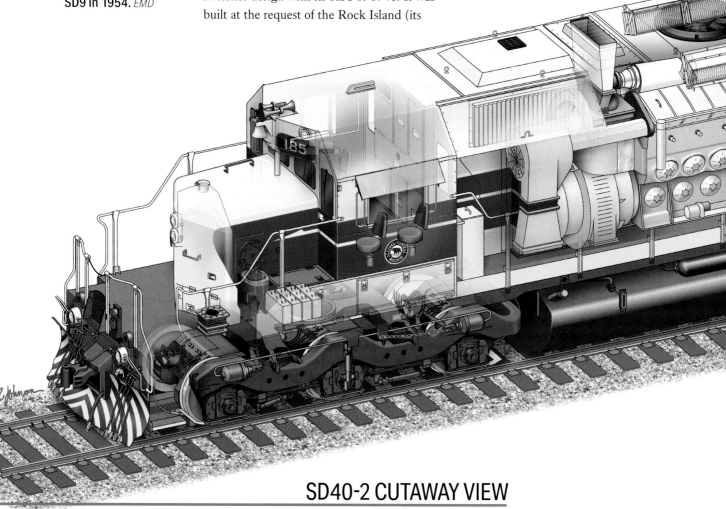

SD40-2 CUTAWAY VIEW

128

trucks. The design provided better visibility in all directions and was a less expensive design to build compared to carbody locomotives. Another chief advantage of the road switcher was improved access to the engine, generator, and other internal components through a series of side doors.

The design would prove popular. Alco introduced the more-powerful RS2 (1,500 hp) in 1946, and Baldwin (DRS-6-4-1500, 1946) and Fairbanks-Morse (H15-44, 1947) were also building road switchers by the time EMD got around to releasing its GP7 in late 1949. Electro-Motive had actually started down the road switcher path with the 1,000-hp NW5 in 1945, but then took a misguided turn to the BL2 (see "EMD's blunder: the BL2" on page 125) before getting it right with the GP7 and later GP9, which sold more than 2,700 and 4,000 copies, respectively. Railroads embraced the utilitarian — but practical and more economical — road-

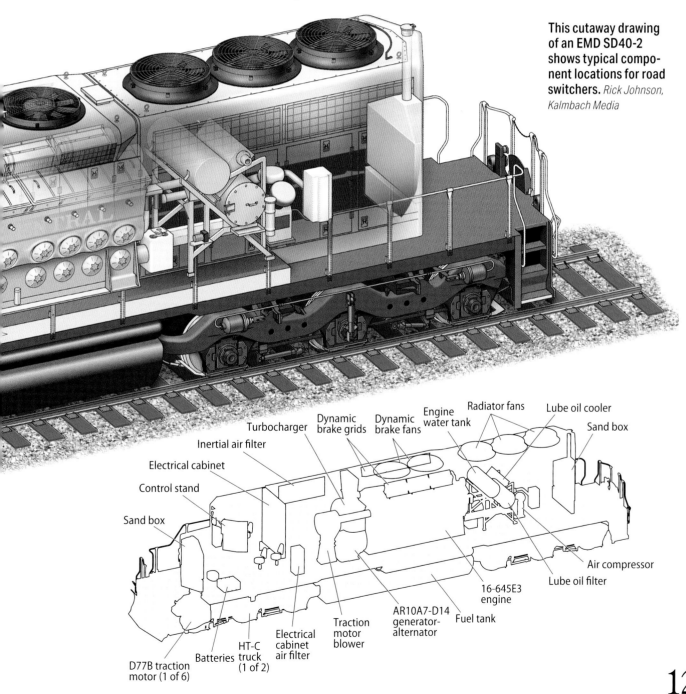

This cutaway drawing of an EMD SD40-2 shows typical component locations for road switchers. *Rick Johnson, Kalmbach Media*

Radiator fans

Lube oil cooler

Sand box

Engine water tank

Dynamic brake fans

Dynamic brake grids

Turbocharger

Inertial air filter

Electrical cabinet

Control stand

Sand box

Air compressor

Lube oil filter

16-645E3 engine

Fuel tank

AR10A7-D14 generator-alternator

Traction motor blower

Electrical cabinet air filter

HT-C truck (1 of 2)

Batteries

D77B traction motor (1 of 6)

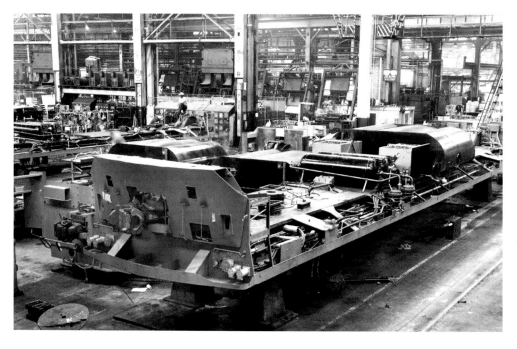

Frames for road switchers are heavy. This GE U25B frame has I beams and cross bearers covered with steel plate, with draft-gear boxes on each end. The hollow middle serves as a conduit for the air/blower system. *General Electric*

switcher design, and by the early 1950s, cab units were on their way out.

The biggest construction difference compared to cab units is the frame, which on road switchers supports everything above it — the body itself is just along for the ride. Frames are fabricated, typically with two parallel steel H-beams as main sills, with multiple cross bearers and a steel plate joining them. Inset from each end is a heavy body bolster, a crosswise member that rides atop each truck. The frame is assembled upside-down, with draft-gear pockets, fuel tank, air reservoirs, and as much wiring and fuel and air plumbing added as possible. The frame is then flipped over to add the engine, generator, cab, body,

and other components. Finally, it is lowered onto its trucks by a crane.

On all road switchers through the late 1950s, the short hood was full height (matching the hood on the engine end). Depending upon manufacturer, this space was used for various ancillary devices, including the steam generator, dynamic brakes, radio gear, and toilet. On most early road switchers, the long hood was designated as the front (rules require

Locomotive assembly starts with the frame upside-down. This view of an EMD F40PH frame shows wiring and piping added, along with air reservoirs and filters, fuel tank, and other components. *EMD*

For major repairs, the entire hood can be removed. Here an Illinois Central GP18 receives a rebuilt EMD 567 engine in the railroad's Paducah, Ky., shops in the early 1970s. *Gary W. Dolzall*

marking the designated front end with a small "F" on that end).

Starting in the late 1950s, manufacturers began offering the option of a low short hood with that end designated as the front. A batch of EMD GP9s for Southern Pacific in 1959 were the first, and GE's U25B demonstrators included both high- and low-nose versions. The increased forward visibility was popular,

and in just a few years the low nose became standard. Norfolk & Western and Southern Railway became the only holdouts, ordering high-nose versions and running locomotives long-hood forward through the 1970s.

The nose and cab continued evolving, with wide-nose versions first appearing in the 1960s on cowl locomotives and on standard road switchers in the 1980s. Improved safety

Many early high-nose road switchers were set up to run long-hood forward. The "F" on the frame marks the locomotive front. This is Alco's DL701 (RS11) demonstrator in 1956. *Alco*

The first road switchers delivered with low noses were EMD GP9s to Southern Pacific in 1959. By the early 1960s, low noses were standard for all builders. *Alan Miller; J. David Ingles collection*

designs (such as stronger interior corner posts and improved anticlimbers) continued evolving into the 2000s. Chapter 8 goes into detail about cab designs.

Minimizing noise in the cab became a focus by the 1980s. EMD first did this by isolating the cab as an option on its SD60 and SD70 lines ("I" suffix). With the SD70ACe-T4, EMD began isolating the engine/main generator instead; GE did the same with its GEVO-engined locomotives.

Most road switchers have historically been single-engine locomotives with a cab near one end. Early variations included center-cab, twin-engine diesels for heavy transfer service, built by Baldwin and Lima-Hamilton. Later double-engine designs were built in the 1960s for fast road-freight service, mainly at request of Union Pacific and Southern Pacific. These included the EMD DD35 and DDA40X, the GE U50 and U50C, and Alco Century 855.

Cowl

Cowl locomotives are full-frame road-switcher locomotives enclosed by a solid shell, or cowl. Unlike earlier carbody style (E, F, PA, FA, etc.) or modern streamlined monocoque passenger locomotives, the sheathing on a cowl locomotive does not contribute to the strength of the frame.

The 1940s saw several railroads order large double-engine, six-axle, center-cab transfer locomotives. Minneapolis, Northfield & Southern No. 23 is a Baldwin DT-6-6-2000; Lima also made similar locomotives. They were designed for slow-speed drag service. *J. David Ingles*

CABLESS LOCOMOTIVES

Cabless locomotives were off-the-shelf options with the first E units of 1937, and remained an option through all builders' carbody-style locomotives (E, F, PA, FA, Sharks, C-Liners). They were almost universally known as "B units." Their design was initially a response to potential claims from operating unions that a locomotive with a cab would require an operating crew. However, even after those issues were settled, railroads continued buying B units through carbody production, both to preserve the smooth appearance of multiple-unit operations and as a cost-saving measure by eliminating the cab.

Even with the coming of road switchers, some cabless locomotives would still be built. Union Pacific was the primary customer, placing orders with EMD for several models, including GP7B, GP9B, GP30B, SD24B, and the biggest of them all, the double-engine DD35. Burlington Northern opted for 120 cabless versions of GE B30-7A diesels (B30-7AB) in 1982-83, and Santa Fe ordered the last B units built, 23 GP60Bs in 1991.

Other than these exceptions, by the 1960s most railroads had decided that any cost savings from cabless diesels wasn't worth the loss in versatility in assigning locomotives.

This four-unit set of Northern Pacific FT freight diesels includes two cabless B units between cab-equipped A units. *Northern Pacific*

Cabless road switchers were rare, but some were built by railroad request. Union Pacific was the largest owner; this is an EMD GP7B just after delivery (it's still awaiting its side lettering). *Union Pacific*

The first cowl locomotives were built by request of the Santa Fe. They were modified six-axle freight locomotives, geared for high speed with steam generators added for passenger service, but enclosed in streamlined sheathing. The initial purposes were to lower wind resistance at high speeds and to continue the streamlined appearance of the passenger trains they'd be pulling; another benefit realized by crews was being sheltered from the elements if they had to go to the engine room during operation — which was especially appreciated in northern climates.

The GE U30CG (mechanically a U30C; the G for "steam generator") was the first, delivered in November 1967. The EMD

FP45 (mechanically an SD45) followed a month later. Milwaukee Road also ordered FP45s, and Santa Fe, Great Northern, and Burlington Northern all bought freight versions (F45s). Other cowl locomotives included the early 1970s passenger GE P30CH (Amtrak) and EMD SDP40F (Amtrak), F40C (Chicago Metra), and F40PH and F59 families (Amtrak and various commuter and regional carriers).

Another variation was a cowl with a tapered indent behind each side of the cab to provide better rearward visibility. These, built for Canadian lines, were nicknamed "Draper Tapers" (named after Canadian National's chief of motive power William L. Draper).

The EMD DDA40X (nicknamed Centennials by sole owner Union Pacific) was the most successful 1960s-era double-engine road switcher. The 6,600-hp locomotive has two 16-cylinder 645E3 engines and rides on four-axle (D) trucks. The first, No. 6900, is shown in its builder's photo (UP adds lettering after delivery). *EMD*

They included the Bombardier HR616 (built in 1982), GMD SD50F, SD60F, and SD40-2F (1985-1988), and the last, the GE C40-8M (1990-1994).

Component layouts

Regardless of body style, a challenge for manufacturers is not only fitting all components into the body, but doing so in a manner that was efficient to build while allowing easy access to components for routine maintenance and heavy repairs.

Since the early 1940s, builders have moved toward modular design and construction as much as possible. Early examples included the move to electrically powered (instead of belt-driven) cooling fans and Electro-Motive making its F2 and later dynamic brake grid/fan a complete assembly as a roof panel. Other examples include

Cowl-style locomotives such as this EMD FP45, with full-width side sheathing, were built at request of the Santa Fe. Unlike cab units, the sides on cowl bodies don't contribute to the frame strength.
Ken Koehler

Amtrak adopted the cowl-body EMD F40PH as its standard passenger locomotive from the mid-1970s through the 1990s. Essentially a cowl version of a GP40-2 with head-end-power and geared for high speed, it was also used by several commuter agencies as well as Via Rail Canada.
Andy Sperandeo

running all wiring through a central electrical cabinet, and in the late 1960s and later employing solid-state electrical and electronic modules that can be easily replaced.

Another example is from EMD's twin-engine E unit production, between the E7 and E8. On the E7, both engines faced to the rear, with their generators toward the cab end. On the E8, the rear engine was flipped, so the generator ends faced out from each other. This, combined with an accessory rack that grouped several components together (oil cooler, oil filter tank, radiator expansion tank, load regulator, and air compressor), freed additional space at the rear of the locomotive, allowing steam generators to have their own compartment. This saved on construction-time hours and eased many maintenance tasks.

Canadian railroads ordered cowl locomotives from multiple builders with tapered sides ("Draper Taper") to improve rearward visibility. This Canadian Pacific GMD SD40-2F was built in 1988.
Trains collection

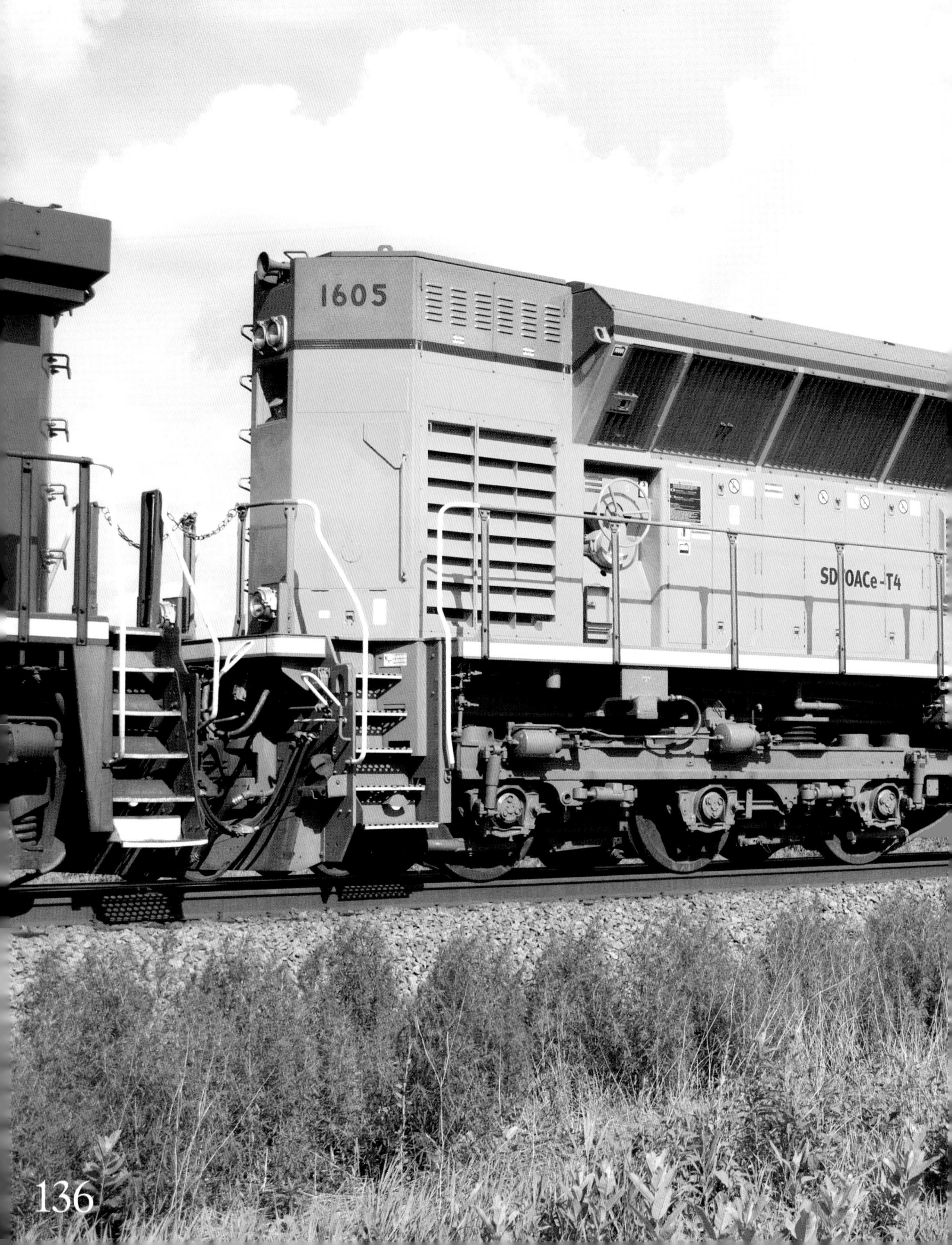
1605

CHAPTER 7

BRAKING SYSTEMS

Diesels employ more than one braking system, all of which are designed to keep the locomotive safe

The rear louvered compartment on this EMD SD70ACe-T4 (just to the rear of the angled radiator wings) houses the dynamic brake grids and fan. The two long cylinders above the side of the fuel tank are the main reservoirs, which supply air to the train's automatic brake system and the locomotive's independent brakes. *Cody Grivno*

Stopping a train is as important — or more important — than getting it into motion. By the time the diesel era began, the automatic air brake was standard equipment. In addition, diesel-electrics were able to use a form of regenerative braking called dynamic braking, which would revolutionize train handling in mountainous areas and on heavy grades.

Braking, in technical terms, is the removal of kinetic energy from a moving object (a train, in our case), and design engineers have all sorts of fancy formulas for determining how much braking power will be required in any given situation based on train speed, weight, rolling resistance, and the length and steepness (percentage) of grade.

In layman's terms, we just need to understand that a train at the top of a grade has a great deal of potential (stored) energy. As much engine/throttle power as was required to get it to the top of that hill will be required in braking power to get it safely to the bottom. Brakes are, of course, necessary in other situations as well, including speed reductions while moving, as

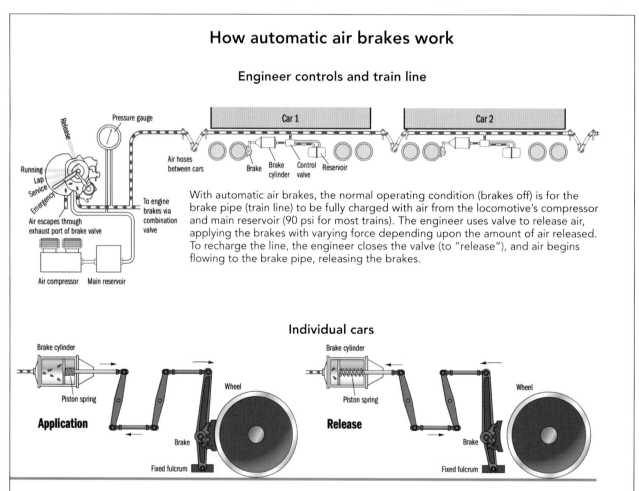

How automatic air brakes work

Engineer controls and train line

With automatic air brakes, the normal operating condition (brakes off) is for the brake pipe (train line) to be fully charged with air from the locomotive's compressor and main reservoir (90 psi for most trains). The engineer uses valve to release air, applying the brakes with varying force depending upon the amount of air released. To recharge the line, the engineer closes the valve (to "release"), and air begins flowing to the brake pipe, releasing the brakes.

Individual cars

When the control valve on each car senses any reduction in brake-pipe pressure, it connects the car's reservoir to the brake cylinder. The cylinder piston is forced outward, setting the brakes by a system of levers that press the brake shoes to the treads on each wheel. When the valve senses an increase in brake-pipe pressure it releases the air from the cylinder; the spring allows the piston to retract, releasing the brakes.

The Canadian National engineer's left hand is on the independent brake valve; the automatic valve (red) is directly above it. His right hand is on the throttle; the dynamic brake lever is directly above that. The box at the top of the control stand on this SD60 is the Trainlink ES system, which, along with communication with the end-of-train device (ETD), allows making brake applications from each end of the train. The brake-pressure gauges are below it and to the right.
Craig Williams

well as any time a train needs to stop.

We'll start by looking at how automatic air brakes work and how engineers control the system's various features. We'll then look at the locomotives' independent brakes and see how traction motors are turned into generators to provide significant braking power.

Air brake operations

George Westinghouse's improved automatic brake system of 1872 revolutionized railroading, allowing faster speeds and longer trains. The basic system remains the same, with many improvements and upgrades to control equipment. The current standard for brake equipment in rolling stock is known as the ABDX system (since 1989), which is the most recent upgrade of the original AB brake system that became mandatory for all new cars as of 1932 (and has progressed through ABD and ABDW). Key improvements of upgraded designs are increased reliability and faster brake response time. The drawing on page 138 shows the basic workings of the system.

Here's how automatic air brakes work:

The brake pipe (often called "train line") is formed by connecting the lines at the ends of each locomotive and car. Flexible hoses with metal couplings ("glad hands") allow this. Air compressors on the locomotives charge the brake pipe; today the standard is 90 pounds per square inch of pressure.

On each car, the control valve (not "triple valve" — those went away with K-type brakes in the steam era) is connected to the train line. The valve performs several functions mechanically, based on sensing pressure changes in the train line. Connected to the control valve is the car's air reservoir, which stores the car's air supply for braking. The reservoir has two halves: auxiliary or service (normal) and emergency. As the train line is charging, the control valve on each car directs air to its reservoir, charging it to the same pressure as the train line.

To make a standard ("service") brake application, the engineer opens the brake valve, allowing air to escape from the train line. The amount of braking is regulated by the amount of air released from the train

HOSE CONNECTIONS AMONG LOCOMOTIVES

The additional air hoses at each end of a diesel locomotive vary by the brake system and by railroad preference. Along with the train line hose (closest to the coupler), there are typically three to five hoses on each side of the pilot, and each side mimics the other. The main reservoir equalizing pipe connects the reservoirs of all locomotives. The brake cylinder equalizing pipe equalizes the independent brake pressure on all locomotives, ensuring that the engine brakes are applied equally on all locomotives operating in a consist (although the air for braking comes from each locomotive's own main reservoir). The actuating pipe signals m.u. locomotives to release their independent brakes without releasing the train brakes. Many railroads use one or two additional hoses to regulate use of locomotive sanders.

This Santa Fe Fairbanks-Morse H16-44 has five hose connections on each side of the coupler (along with the main train line hose). On the ride side, starting at the coupler, are the train line hose; main reservoir equalizing; actuating; actuating release; front sander; and rear sander. *Santa Fe*

line: A 12-pound reduction, for example, provides stronger braking than an 8-pound reduction.

The control valve on each car senses the drop in pressure and directs a corresponding percentage of air from the service portion of its car's reservoir into the brake cylinder. Air entering the brake cylinder forces the piston out from the end of the cylinder. The piston, via levers, pushes the brake shoes against the wheel treads, applying the brakes.

To release the brakes, the engineer closes the brake valve; the main reservoir begins recharging air in the train line. When the control valves on the cars sense the increase in pressure, they release the brakes (by releasing air from the cylinders) and begin recharging individual cars' brake reservoirs.

Locomotive controls

Locomotive control valves and equipment standards (called "schedules") have also evolved. Early diesel switchers had No. 6 equipment, with 6BL and 6SL schedules on early road diesels. Schedule 24RL became standard in the mid-1940s, schedule 26L in 1957, and schedule 30 is standard on modern diesels with desktop controls (see Chapter 8 for additional examples). Each reflects upgrades in control features; many locomotives retain their original brake controls, and locomotives of varying brake schedules can operate together in multiple-unit fashion.

The engineer controls the automatic brakes using a handle on the brake stand in the cab. The handle travels through an arc; the specific functions vary from the schedule 6 through schedule 30 controls, but the basic operation is similar.

Here's a summary of the controls, with handle positions from left to right as you look at the arc of the handle (see the drawing on page 138):

Release: Connects the main reservoir to the brake pipe until the brake pipe reaches the desired pressure (90 pounds per square inch on modern freight trains).

Running: Maintains the running pressure

Brake gauges are standardized. The gauge at left shows the pressure in the main reservoir and equalizing reservoir, the middle gauge shows brake cylinder and brake pipe pressure, and the gauge at right shows the air flow rate in the brake pipe.
Steve Smedley

The brakes on this EMD radial (steerable) truck are applied: The pistons on the brake cylinders are extended (note the polished areas on the pistons from movement) and the brake shoes are firmly against the wheels. *Cody Grivno*

This three-cylinder, two-stage compressor, installed in an Electro-Motive FT, supplies air to the main reservoir.
EMD

in the brake pipe by routing air from the feed valve as needed to compensate for minor losses from leaks. (Modern brake systems eliminate this; the "release" setting now automatically does this.)

Lap: Closes the connection between the main reservoir and brake pipe, and closes the connection from train pipe to atmosphere after an application. This keeps the brakes applied at the desired level. (Modern brake systems, from 26L and later, don't have this setting and are said to be "self-lapping;" that is, they hold the desired level of application applied until they are released.)

Application: Opens the connection from the train line to atmosphere via the equalizing reservoir, reducing the brake-pipe pressure to the desired level for braking.

Emergency: Opens the brake pipe directly to atmosphere to apply full braking force.

Gauges: Brake pressures are shown on

two displays on the engineer's control stand, each of which have two needle gauges. One shows the main reservoir and equalizing reservoir pressures; the second shows the train line (brake pipe) and brake cylinder pressures. Another gauge, the brake pipe flow indicator, shows the rate of air flow into the train line. Modern locomotives show this on computer terminal displays.

A minimum service reduction is 6 to 8 pounds; this is often done to control slack action before using a stronger application. A maximum reduction (with a 90-pounds per square inch train line) is 26 pounds, which is known as a "full-service application."

A key in handling air brakes is that following a brake application and release, it takes several minutes for the train line and each car's reservoir to recharge. The specific time varies by the strength of the original application, the length of the train,

temperature (the colder it is, the more leaks will occur at gaskets and joints), and number of locomotives/air compressors. If an engineer initiates a second application before the system has recharged from an initial application, there will be less braking power available. In extreme situations, this can result in limited or no service brakes being applied, which can result in having to employ the emergency brakes to stop the train. Engineers have a crude-but-accurate term for doing this, the PG-rated version of which would be "piddling away your air."

To make an emergency application, all of the air is released from the train line (known as "big-holing" the brakes). Sensing this, the control valves move all the air from each car's reservoir, including the emergency portion, to the cylinders, providing a maximum application. This is what provides the key safety feature with automatic brakes: Any

broken hose or failure of the air line (such as if a coupler knuckle or drawbar breaks or other situation causes the train to break in two, separating the air hoses) causes an instant drop in pressure, which automatically triggers an emergency brake application.

Passenger trains often operate at higher brake pressure (110 pounds per square inch). Some railroads operating in mountainous territory will run with the higher brake pressure as well. In the early diesel era, 70 pounds per square inch was typical for freight trains. In the same period, 90 pounds per square inch for passenger service was normal. The increased pressure adds a measure of safety for longer, faster trains, but requires more power (and time) to charge. The brake pipe operating pressure is set by a regulating valve on the rear of the brake control stand (it's not adjusted during routine train operations).

The main reservoir comprises two air cylinders that can be mounted under the frame, as on this GE locomotive under construction, alongside the fuel tank, or on the roof. *Robert Hale*

The air system includes filters, a moisture trap, and safety valves. The ends of the main reservoir cylinders are visible behind the filters on this General Electric Dash 8-40BW, with the fuel tank and bell at left. *Cody Grivno*

Some leakage is inevitable along the brake pipe because of train length and the numerous joints and connections. The maximum allowable difference between the locomotive and end of the train is 15 pounds. The rear pressure is monitored by the end-of-train device (EOTD or ETD), and by a gauge in the caboose through the 1970s.

Once applied, the brakes on a freight train cannot be partially released — if a release is initiated, they have to be allowed to release fully. Some passenger equipment allows a partial brake release.

The advent of "smart ETDs" — ETDs that can both send and receive information and commands from the cab — has allowed the option of applying brakes from both ends of a train simultaneously. Since the 1990s, some systems allow sending signals to the ETD that enables them to release air from the train line to mimic the brake application being applied from the cab (Wabtec's Trainlink ES is one system). This results in faster response throughout the train with less slack action (especially welcome for long, heavy trains).

Independent brake

The independent brake is the air brake system on the locomotive itself (or locomotives, if two or more are in multiple-unit operation). Applying this brake is independent of the train brakes, hence the name. Each locomotive truck has one or more brake cylinders on each side to control the brake shoes (one or two per wheel).

The independent brake is controlled by a valve handle on the control stand separate from the automatic valve. The independent brake is a "straight air" system, meaning air released from the main reservoir goes directly to the locomotive's brake cylinder. This means it is fast-acting and sensitive, so engineers must use care not to apply brakes too heavily, which can cause wheels to skid. The handle varies the amount of air from fully released to fully applied, which is used essentially as a parking brake (provided that the engine is running and the compressor is operating).

The locomotive's brakes are also applied during an automatic brake application; the independent valve allows an engineer to bypass this, if desired, for better control.

Compressor and reservoir

The air supply for the brake system comes from a compressor located in the engine room. Most locomotive air compressors are three-cylinder, two-stage designs, usually driven directly from the engine driveshaft. Two-stage means the

Dynamic brake grids on EMD hood units into the 1980s were located in flared housings along the roof of the hood, as on this Santa Fe loco- motive. *Joe McMillan*

ELECTROPNEUMATIC BRAKES

A limitation of automatic air brakes is response time: It takes several seconds per car for air-pressure changes to travel through the brake pipe to signal response from cars, causing uneven train handling (especially problematic on long, heavy trains). With electropneumatic braking, air is still supplied through the brake pipe for braking, but electrical signals passed through the train are used to signal brake applications on each car. The result is instantaneous response from all cars, providing smoother brake handling.

The Association of American Railroads adopted its standard S-4200 covering these systems in 1999 (and has revised it multiple times since then). Now commonly known as "electronically controlled pneumatic" (ECP) braking, as defined by the AAR, an ECP system: " ... is a train power braking system actuated by compressed air and controlled by electronic signals originated at the locomotive for service and emergency applications. The brake pipe is used to supply a constant supply of air to the reservoirs." The last part is another key, in that the brake pipe can maintain a constant pressure, instead of having to vary the pressure to pass braking signals to trailing cars. A two-conductor electric line ("cable") transmits electrical signals through the train, requiring compatible connectors throughout.

Electropneumatic systems have been used in some applications since the 1930s, including a few early diesel streamliners. Since then, all uses have been in passenger service, where rolling stock is largely captive and fleets are relatively small. The expense of adding ECP systems to all freight equipment is an issue, along with developing common standards for their use. Experiments continue, and both Wabtec and New York Air Brake have developed approved systems.

This new GP60M in 1990 shows how EMD uses fans in external housings on the roof for the dynamic brake (center) and radiator (far right). They pull air in through the side grilles and expel it upward. The diesel engine exhaust stack is at left. *EMD*

air is initially compressed by a pair of low-pressure cylinders, which compress air to about 40 pounds per square inch. The air is then compounded, passes through an intercooler (air being compressed becomes hot and expands), then through a high-pressure cylinder. The compressor can be cooled by air or water.

This compressed air is routed to the main reservoir, which comprises two cylindrical, rounded-end storage tanks (main reservoirs Nos. 1 and 2). The two tanks provide redundancy, and check valves ensure that a failure of one reservoir tank does not affect the other. Reservoirs vary in location by locomotive manufacturer and model. They can be placed under the frame transversely next to the fuel tank, longitudinally next to or above the sides of the fuel tank, or on the roof. The piping from the compressor to the reservoir often doubles back on itself, serving as a cooling coil — a longer path that further cools the compressed air.

Although the engine-driven compressor runs continually, it is only actively pumping when needed. An electro-pneumatic

governor on the compressor turns the pump on and off to maintain the proper air pressure (usually 140 pounds per square inch — the main reservoir must be at least 15 psi above the normal operating pressure of the brake pipe). When operating in m.u. with other locomotives, all locomotives' reservoirs and compressors are working together to supply the train line.

The reservoir system is equipped with a safety valve to allow venting excess pressure. The system also has multiple filters and a valve to eliminate condensed water that forms in the system as air cools. This valve is automatic on modern diesels: If you've ever stood near a locomotive and heard an occasional "pssh" sound, that's moisture being blown from the system. On early diesels, this was done manually by opening a valve.

The equalizing reservoir is a small tank located between the main reservoir and the brake pipe. Its pressure is the same as the desired pressure of the brake pipe. In making a brake application, air is released from the equalizing reservoir, which triggers a valve to release air from the brake pipe until its pressure equals that in the equalizing reservoir.

Although the main use of the air system is braking (and it's the sole duty of the No. 2 main reservoir), air is also used for the horn, sanders, and on many locomotives, to actuate the bell ringer and windshield wipers.

Dynamic braking

Dynamic braking gave diesel-electric locomotives a big operational advantage over steam in mountains and other lines with long and/or steep grades. The basic idea is that a locomotive's traction motors are turned into generators, which provides a great deal of rolling resistance — enough to hold train speeds in check on a grade, often without using automatic brakes. This results in not only better, smoother train handling, but saves brake-shoe wear and eliminates overheating and damage that can occur to wheels from the heavy braking. Dynamic brakes are mechanically separate from the air-brake systems, but they can be used together.

The system is based on the regenerative braking feature of electric locomotives, which had been successfully used since the early 1900s. In regenerative braking, the electricity produced by the traction motors during braking is returned to the overhead wire. In dynamic braking on a diesel-electric, the electricity produced is run through banks of resistors and dissipated as heat.

Dynamic braking became optional on diesels from the early 1940s onward, and was originally primarily chosen by railroads operating in mountainous areas. Flatland and prairie railroads often opted to save the expense and purchased non-dynamic-equipped locomotives, and yard and passenger diesels rarely had dynamics. Dynamics have became standard equipment on modern locomotives (from the 1990s onward).

In technical terms, in dynamic braking the traction motor fields are energized, which turns the motors into generators. The

On early GE hood units (through Dash-7 locomotives) the dynamic brake (resistor) grid was behind the radiator air intake screen at the rear of the hood. The same fans that cooled the radiator cooled the grids. This is a Milwaukee Road U33C.
Louis A. Marre

motors/generators must have an electrical load — hence the resistor banks — to provide the rolling resistance. Without a load on the generators, there's no resistance.

Dynamic braking has evolved substantially since it was introduced. The first road locomotive to use it was Electro-Motive's FT, at the insistence of the Santa Fe. The initial system was limited, providing just two settings for high or low braking power. Early in FT production this was improved to allow a complete range of control from off to full braking power.

Into the 1970s, the effective speed range for dynamic braking was about 18 to 25 mph. At that time, manufacturers developed "extended-range" dynamics as an option, which provided effective braking power down to 8 mph. The advent of AC traction motors greatly improved dynamic brake functions, and today's AC locomotives can effectively use dynamic brakes under 1 mph.

Dynamic brakes are a high-maintenance item, as the heat generated can eventually burn out resistor grids, and fans see heavy use to cool the grids. Older road locomotives reassigned to local and yard service, or sold to regional or shortline railroads, often have their dynamic brakes disconnected as a cost-saving measure.

Dynamic brake grids and control

The large banks of resistors required to dissipate heat require one or more fans to provide cooling, and these housings and fans can be distinctive spotting features on locomotives. Their locations vary widely among manufacturer, model, and era.

Electro-Motive F2 and later cab units had a ceiling-panel-mounted dynamic brake unit just behind the cab (center of the roof on FTs). On EMD road switchers through 60-series locomotives, dynamics were housed in a blister in middle of the roof, marked by overhanging, angled wings with grille coverings. Early GE road switchers had grids placed vertically behind the screened radiator air intake openings at the rear of the long hood. Modern road switchers have dynamics located either directly behind the cab or at the end of the hood, marked by louvered or grilled openings.

On Alco hood units, dynamics were placed in the nose of early RS-series diesels, and along the middle of the hood on later RS and Century road switchers (marked by rectangular screened openings — see the RS11 on page 131 in Chapter 6). Baldwin road switchers also had them in the nose. Fairbanks-Morse mounted the grids at roof level just behind the cab.

Dynamic brake fans could be in separate housings visible on the roof, or located under the roof above the grid.

The controls for dynamic brakes are on the engineer's control stand, although the exact design varied among manufacturers, locomotive models, and eras. Most newer control stands have a separate dynamic-brake control lever, while others use the throttle lever to regulate dynamics (with a separate "power/brake" switch that allows selecting the function of the throttle lever). See Chapter 8 for examples of several cab-control layouts.

In any case, the engineer engages the dynamics by placing the throttle in idle

while the train is operating within the prescribed speed range. After allowing several seconds, the controller (throttle or separate lever) is notched out, basically in a reverse manner of applying the throttle when starting. The dynamic brake force can be adjusted to maintain the desired speed, which again must be within the system's range. Moving the controller adds progressively more resistors to the circuit with each setting; the more electrical resistance that's added, the more electrical power the motors are forced to generate, and the greater the rolling resistance.

The ammeter (on a DC-traction locomotive) shows the current generated; this gauge is usually a zero-center dial that shows power in one direction and braking in the other. On an AC-traction locomotive, this is shown by the traction meter.

If a train in full dynamic braking begins

increasing in speed, the engineer may add a service application of the automatic brakes to keep train speed in check. Whether this is needed depends on train speed and weight, rail conditions, steepness of grade, and the total braking power available (number of locomotives).

When operating in MU, all locomotives in a consist will respond to braking commands from the lead locomotive. Locomotives not equipped with dynamics may still be operated in MU with dynamic-equipped locomotives, but obviously only those with dynamics will respond (and a dynamic-brake equipped locomotive must be leading). Since the 1960s, consists of locomotives of mixed builders (GE and EMD) will operate together with dynamics; for earlier diesels, it depends upon the exact system being used. Railroads sometimes modified dynamic brake systems and m.u.

connections to make this work, or called out in their special instructions the locomotives that were and weren't compatible.

Hand brake

As with rolling stock, locomotives have a hand-operated brake wheel (or lever-style handle) that can be used to apply brakes. This is generally located on the side of the nose and on the side of the end of the long hood on road switchers. Cab units often have the brake wheel or handle inside the locomotive (cab and/or engine room). Turning the wheel pulls the piston out from the brake cylinder, applying the brake shoes to the wheel treads. These are typically used when parking locomotives for an extended time. Chapter 9 (page 172) shows one example; others can be seen in photos throughout the book.

Early Alco hood units with dynamic brakes had the grids in the short hood, which on locomotives also equipped with steam generators required extending the roof to cab-roof level. This is a Lehigh Valley RS3 (nicknamed a "hammerhead").
Richard W. Story

CHAPTER 8

CAB DESIGN & LOCOMOTIVE CONTROLS

While cab design has changed over the decades, basic controls remain virtually the same

The engineer of an Amtrak GE Genesis-series locomotive has the Auto Train running at 69 mph in February 2012 as the road foreman of engines looks on. The locomotive features desktop controls and computer screens to display operating data. *Al DiCenso*

The bare-bones control stands and spartan cabs of the 1940s have given way to modern designs featuring console controls and computer-screen displays. The actual operation of most locomotive controls, however, remains much the same. An engineer from 1942 dropped into a locomotive cab in 2023 would — after a bit of initial shock — quickly be able to figure out how to get a train rolling.

Regardless of whether a diesel-electric locomotive is from the pre-microprocessor era or today, it has these controls in the engineer's cab area: throttle lever; reverser; dynamic brake lever (on engines so equipped); and automatic and independent air brake levers. An assortment of switches, valves, and levers control items such as the horn, bell, sanders, lights (including headlights, classification lights, panel gauge lights, and interior lights), windshield wipers, cab heater, fuel pump, and steam

generator (if equipped). Gauges and monitor lights include speedometer, ammeter, brake-system pressure gauges, and warning lights for wheel slip, oil pressure, engine temperature, and electrical ground relay.

The rear cab wall generally houses the electrical cabinet, and will have lesser-used switches and controls: fuel pump, engine shutdown, and switches for isolating the locomotive or traction motors. It also includes additional warning lights, switches, breakers, fuses, and relays.

Two-way radios became common from the 1950s onward, and can be handset (telephone) or microphone style. Additional control equipment includes controls for end-of-train devices (1980s and later), remote radio control for helper locomotives (starting in the 1960s on some railroads), and cab signals (on some railroads and routes).

Cabs on switchers and road switchers are enclosed. Traditional cabs have access doors on the front left and rear right, opening to the front and side walkways (running

This BNSF General Electric ES44DC, built in 2007, features a traditional control stand with multiple computer displays. The screen at top left is the positive train control (PTC) display. The front left screen is Wabtec's Trip Optimizer display; other displays show speed, brake air, and system status information. *Stan Henderson*

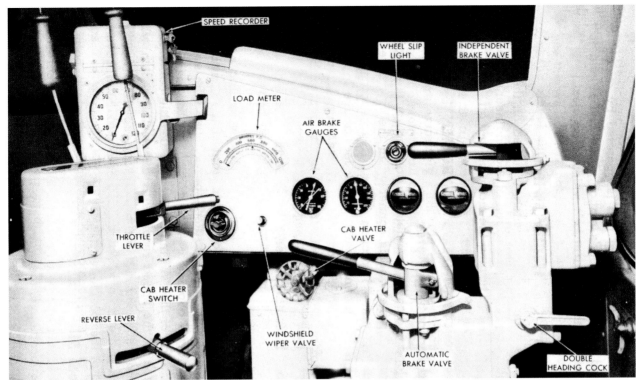

Labels on image: SPEED RECORDER, WHEEL SLIP LIGHT, INDEPENDENT BRAKE VALVE, LOAD METER, AIR BRAKE GAUGES, THROTTLE LEVER, CAB HEATER VALVE, CAB HEATER SWITCH, REVERSE LEVER, WINDSHIELD WIPER VALVE, AUTOMATIC BRAKE VALVE, DOUBLE HEADING COCK

This is the engineer's side of the cab on an EMD F unit from the 1940s. Although the layout is different compared to a modern locomotive, the basic controls — throttle and brakes — remain the same. *EMD*

boards). Those with wide noses have the front access door through the nose (which also usually contains a retention or chemical toilet — these are mandatory on modern road locomotives).

The cabs on carbody-style locomotives have side access doors with vertical steps directly below them. The cabs are isolated from the engine room by a wall that usually also includes an electrical cabinet. They have one or two doors on the rear cab wall to access the engine room.

The specific cab interior layout, including seats, operating consoles, and window arrangement, varies widely among locomotives by type (switcher, cab unit, road switcher), manufacturer, specific model, era, and also varies with railroad-specific options and choices. Let's take a look at some early cab setups, then move to more modern designs.

Early diesels

As with steam locomotives, diesels are set up so that the engineer occupies the right-hand seat when facing forward. The first road diesels (passenger and later freight cab units)

had on the engineer's side a control panel dashboard that included gauges (brake system and ammeter) and basic control switches and warning lights. The throttle and transition selector were located in a large barrel-shaped stand to the engineer's left. Pulling back on the throttle increases speed. The brake stand, with the automatic and independent handles, were in front and slightly to the right.

The left side is usually rather plain, with just a seat for the fireman. The dash area may have steam-generator controls (on locomotives that had them) and possibly some warning lights. Another seat to the rear was often provided for the head-end brakeman.

All locomotives are equipped with an "alerter" system and device, designed to ensure that the engineer hasn't fallen asleep or become inattentive. The most-common device on early diesels was a foot-switch pedal, often called a "dead-man's pedal." It's located on the floor in front of the engineer's seat, and has to be depressed at all times for the locomotive to operate. Releasing the pedal for more than a few seconds triggers an alarm and then an automatic brake application.

You're looking over the shoulder of the engineer on an EMD F unit doing 49 mph on the Western Pacific near Tracy, Calif. Engineers praised F units for their great forward visibility. The engineer's left hand is on the throttle; the transition lever is to the left, on the other side of the control stand, and the brake lever is at lower right.
Ted Benson

Horns on early diesels were typically controlled by handles on ropes to the engineer's left. On a locomotive with two horns — single-note versions pointing fore and aft — there was a separate rope for each. For a locomotive with a multi-chime horn, one rope controlled the whole horn.

Engineers loved cab units for their panoramic views, with wide windshields and high vantage point overlooking a short nose, providing a clear view forward. They did not, however, like having to perform switching or reverse moves with cab units. The only way to see clearly to the rear was to stick your head out the window, which also involved some contortions while trying to reach the operating controls.

With road switchers, controls and gauges moved to a large vertical console to the engineer's left. The throttle control was typically to the right, with the brake stand moved to the left. This allowed the engineer to more easily turn in the chair to see out the rear cab window while keeping all controls in easy

The well-worn cab of a high-nose EMD GP7 shows the same basic components of an F unit, but a different layout, with the throttle stand at right, brake controls at center and left, and gauges and switches on the tall control panel in the middle. The telephone-style radio at upper left was a common add-on from the 1950s onward.
Donald R. Kaplan

reach, providing more comfortable operation. Visibility was not as good to the front as with cab units, since early road switchers had high noses (low noses wouldn't appear until 1959) and most were set up to operate long-hood forward. Some railroads ordered road switchers with dual control stands, allowing easy operation in either direction without having to turn the locomotive.

With the 1960s shift to low noses — and with that end now the front — control stands typically were shifted more toward the front, but with all controls still to the left of the small windshield directly in front of the engineer. By the 1970s, controls remained in the same basic positions, but manufacturers were giving control stands a more streamlined, modern look, with more labeling of controls and upgraded designs for levers and controls.

This evolution included radios, which were now often integrated to the control stand instead of being added atop it, and the horn, which became more commonly

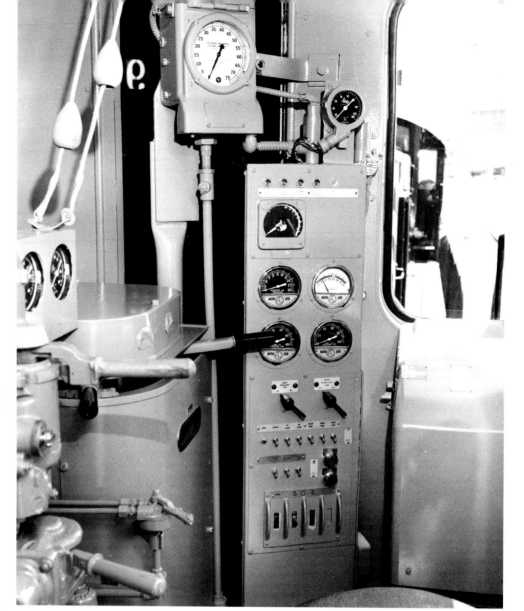

This is the cab of an Alco high-nose road switcher in 1961. Brake handles and gauges are to the left, the throttle lever at center, and horn ropes at upper left. The front panel has temperature and pressure gauges for the oil, water, and fuel systems, plus various warning lights and control switches, with the speedometer at top center. The cab heater is below the windshield. *Alco*

controlled by a spring-loaded lever instead of a rope. In place of pedal-style alerters, railroads began opting for hand switches that must be touched when an alert sounds.

Cab signals, automatic train stop

An innovation of the 1920s was cab signaling. Coded electrical signals sent through the track are picked up by induction sensors on the locomotive, translated, and shown on a display in the cab. Known as pulse-code cab signaling, it was developed by Union Switch & Signal and widely adopted initially by the Pennsylvania Railroad. Many railroads eliminated wayside signals along routes where cab signaling was in place. The photo on page 159 shows a PRR GG1 position-light cab signal; the image of a Union Pacific SD60M on page 160 shows a modern cab signal installation between front windows with displays visible to both the engineer and conductor.

Another form of control used by many railroads was automatic train stop (ATS), developed in the 1920s by General Railway Signal. This system used truck-mounted sensors that were triggered when a train passed a restrictive signal. An alarm sounded in the cab; the engineer had to acknowledge the alarm or a brake application was initiated. Cab signals or ATS were required for trains on routes hosting high-speed trains (faster than 79 mph). The use of either

Engineer Fred Wein is at the controls of a Milwaukee Road Fairbanks-Morse H12-44 switcher while talking to a brakeman on a handheld radio in 1978. *Gary W. Dolzall*

The advent of low noses on road switchers greatly improved visibility. This is a low-nose GE U25B in 1962. The GE throttle (directly in front of the engineer) has additional settings in between the previous standard of eight notches; the dynamic brake lever is left of the throttle and the brake levers at far left. *General Electric*

On GE's initial high-hood version of its U25B, the throttle stand hung down from the cab ceiling. This view from the front window shows the engineer with his hand on the throttle and shows the cab back wall/electrical cabinet with control switches.
General Electric

along a route so equipped meant that the lead locomotive in any consist had to be equipped with cab signals/ATS.

Both systems have now largely been superseded with the advent of positive train control (PTC).

Desktop controls and computer screens

The first microprocessor-equipped locomotives, EMD's GP/SD60 series and GE's Dash-8 line of the 1980s, saw the broad adaptation of wide-nose "safety cab" designs and with them, the first desktop-style throttle and brake controls. Typical layout is to have the independent and automatic brake handles grouped together at the right; to their left is a single handle controlling the throttle and dynamic brakes, plus a reverser handle. Computer screens soon followed, usually placed on the console in front of the engineer, with screens sometimes atop the control stand. The screens replaced most analog gauges, with switches on or below the panels controlling most functions that had been on

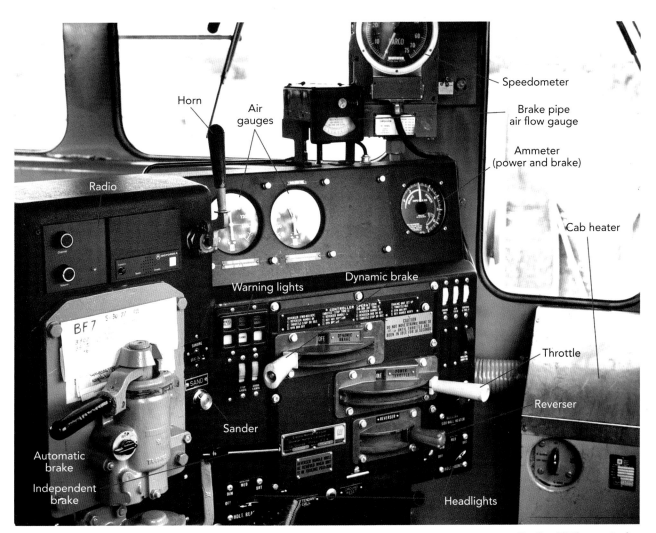

Horn

Air gauges

Speedometer

Brake pipe air flow gauge

Ammeter (power and brake)

Radio

Cab heater

Warning lights

Dynamic brake

Throttle

Sander

Reverser

Automatic brake

Independent brake

Headlights

By the 1970s, control stands were becoming more refined and better organized. This is a new Conrail GP40-2 built in 1977. *Conrail*

Cab signals — at left on this Pennsylvania Railroad GG1 electric locomotive — mimic lineside signals, using electrical codes sent through the rails. These show "clear" on Pennsy's position-light-style signals. *Pennsylvania Railroad*

159

This EMD SD60M, built in 1989, was among the first locomotives to feature desktop-style controls. The brake controls are at far right, with the throttle and reverser directly in front of the engineer. Conventional gauges are still used — computer screens are still a few years away. A cab signal is mounted between the windshields at left.

Union Pacific

the conventional control stand. The cab's left side featured a desk for the conductor, with a computer screen repeating the status of various systems.

Desktop controls, although sleek, met with mixed reviews from operating crews. Forward running is usually fine, with good visibility. However, doing reverse moves — not to mention switching — can be challenging. Some railroads continued ordering locomotives with conventional control stands; others went back to them after initially ordering desktop controls.

A redesign came when EMD released its SD70ACe in 2004. The advent of AC traction controls meant more (and more-advanced) computer systems. The new

EMD stand had controls in a panel to the engineer's left like a traditional road switcher, but in a refined, streamlined design compared to earlier locomotives. Rounded corners and elimination of sharp edges made for a safer environment. The desktop front was retained, but for computer displays and a place for a clipboard and paperwork.

Another improvement on new locomotives was improving the view from the cab by angling the nose downward and adjusting the cab seats to allow better visibility. Even with the advent of low-nose road switchers in the 1960s, visibility was often not ideal, and impeded by the nose itself as well as controls placed along the front wall.

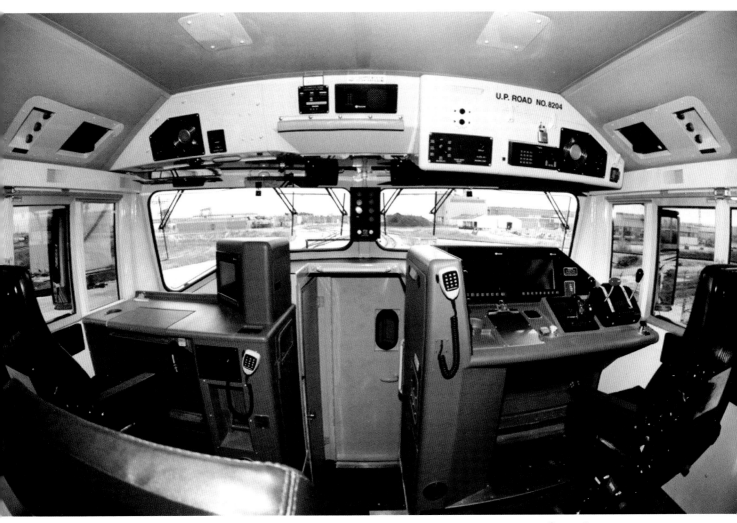

Additional controls on modern locomotives have included a head-of-train unit (HOT box) that sends and receives information from the end-of-train device (EOTD or ETD), including brake pressure, motion status, marker light status, remaining battery, and communication status. This controller can send a command to the ETD to apply emergency braking if needed, and some systems allow the ETD to aid making service applications as well (see Chapter 7). New locomotives have this control integrated to the stand; it was a separate add-on for earlier locomotives.

The coming of positive train control (PTC), in service on most routes by the end of 2020, added another display to the cab (see more on PTC in Chapter 3). The system analyzes the locations of all trains and monitors train speeds and speed restrictions to avoid collisions and dangerous situations. Systems include Alstom's Incremental Train Control System (ITCS) and Wabtec's Positive Train Control Interoperable Electronic Train Management System (I-ETMS). The PTC display can be a simple digital readout, showing legal track speed, current signal indication, and current status, or include a full-screen display showing a track schematic and train statuses.

Yet another software package (and display screen) on some locomotives works to manage fuel use and engine efficiency.

Computer screens along with desktop controls were common by the time this Union Pacific SD9043MAC was built in 1998. The coming of AC traction meant increased microprocessor controls. This view shows the conductor's desk and screen at left, and the door down into the nose (and toilet) at center. *Union Pacific*

The screen on this ex-Union Pacific SD9043MAC running on the Indiana Railroad in 2009 displays speed, braking information, throttle setting, tractive effort, acceleration rate, reverser status, train length, and fuel level. It would also show cab signal status if that system were used on this line.

Eric Powell

This Norfolk Southern GE ES40DC has display screens mounted atop the control stand. The screen at the left is the standard display terminal; the screen at right is the LEADER (Locomotive Engineer Assist/Display and Event Recorder) display. LEADER is New York Air Brake's train-handling efficiency program. *David Lester*

Wabtec's version is called Trip Optimizer; New York Air Brake offers its LEADER system. These systems function as a type of cruise control, but also factor in route profile (grades and curves), speed zones, and desired arrival time to adjust throttle and brake settings.

Railroads can upgrade older locomotives with various microprocessor controls, which are available as add-ons from locomotive manufacturers and third-party vendors. These can include wheel-slip control, advanced dynamic-brake control, fuel monitoring, automatic engine start/stop,

and engine and systems diagnostics. Add-on systems require a computer in the electrical cabinet, with sensors as needed throughout the locomotive as described in Chapter 4.

Radio-control helpers and distributed-power units (DPUs)

Helper locomotives (and helper districts, the specific areas where they operate) have been a part of railroading since the 1800s. The combination of diesel-electric locomotives and improved radio technology led to radio-controlled helpers in the 1960s. The first common system (and one that's

Opposite page: Traditional-style control stands made a comeback by the early 2000s. This new EMD SD70ACe in 2013 has a modernized tall stand at left (rounded corners and edges for safety) with brake controls at left and dynamic brake, throttle, and reverser in the middle. The desktop features computer displays for system data and statuses. *Jim Wrinn*

163

This is the basic control/display panel for the positive train control (PTC) and automatic train control (ATC) panel systems as used on SEPTA (Southeastern Pennsylvania Transportation Authority) locomotives.
Brian Solomon

When using radio-controlled remote locomotives, the engineer on the lead (control) locomotive has the option of having the remote locomotives mimic the controls of the lead locomotive (display screen at left) or operating the remote engines independently (right) by "setting up the wall" (vertical line on display separating the locomotive groups).
General Electric

MOVEMENT AUTHORITY
CLEAR

MAXIMUM AUTHORIZED SPEED
50
ATC   PTC

OVERSPEED   ACTUAL SPEED
47   NO VALID
            TSR DATA

ATC CUT-IN   PTC CUT-IN
ATC CUT-OUT   PTC CUT-OUT
ATC FAILURE   PTC FAILURE
ERS FAILURE   VALID DATABASE
SUPPRESSION

MESSAGE   MESSAGE DISPLAY
SELECT

ALERTER BRIGHTNESS "C" SIGNAL

PTC   ATC
DEPARTURE   DEPARTURE
TEST   TEST

still widely used) is Locotrol, pioneered by the Southern Railway. The system was eventually acquired by General Electric.

Locomotives designated as lead or control units were equipped with controls and radio equipment. With many early operations, a control car (converted locomotive shell or boxcar) was used to house the radio receiver and control equipment for the remote locomotives. This way, locomotives used as helpers (in-train or at the rear) didn't have to be specially equipped — any locomotive (or consist) connected to the control car would receive commands from the lead locomotive. Individual locomotives could also be equipped with receivers, which became common as system technology advanced; a single locomotive so equipped would pass signals to locomotives connected to it in m.u. fashion. Additional railroads adopting the system soon included Canadian Pacific, Kansas City Southern, Norfolk & Western, Santa Fe, Southern Pacific, and Union Pacific.

The use of remote locomotives proved popular and spread beyond routes with stiff grades and helper districts. Since the 1990s it has become increasingly common for railroads to add locomotives within the train

22:09:30	A-1000	B-2000
RUN		
THROTTLE	T4	T4
LOAD	0A	0A
BP	90	89
FLOW	63	0
REMOTE		NORM
ER	90	90
CYLINDER	0	0
MAIN RES	105	107
	BACK	REMOTE SAND / REMOTE MENU

23:08:52	A-1000	B-2000
RUN		
THROTTLE	T2	T2
LOAD	0A	0A
BP	91	90
FLOW	17	0
REMOTE		NORM
ER	90	90
CYLINDER	0	0
MAIN RES	111	112
FRONT	IDLE	TRCTN - / TRCTN + / REMOTE SAND / RE...

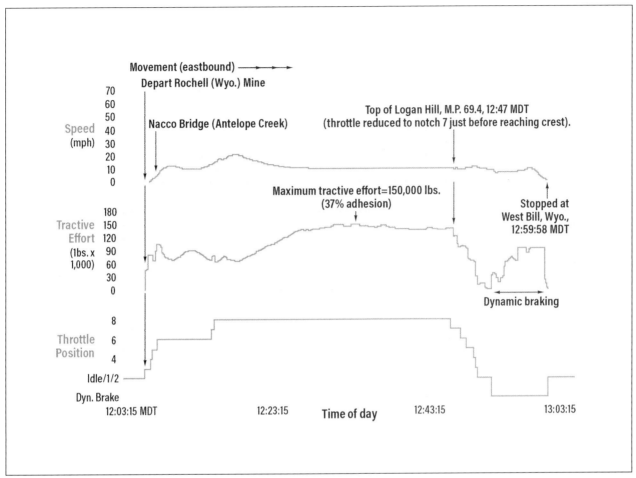

Movement (eastbound) ⟶ ⟶
Depart Rochell (Wyo.) Mine

Speed (mph)

Nacco Bridge (Antelope Creek)

Top of Logan Hill, M.P. 69.4, 12:47 MDT
(throttle reduced to notch 7 just before reaching crest).

Tractive Effort (lbs. x 1,000)

Maximum tractive effort=150,000 lbs.
(37% adhesion)

Stopped at West Bill, Wyo., 12:59:58 MDT

Dynamic braking

Throttle Position

12:03:15 MDT   12:23:15   Time of day   12:43:15   13:03:15

for its entire trip, not just in a helper district. This is known as distributed power (DP), and the locomotives operating remotely are known as distributed power units (DPUs). The use of DPUs allows railroads to run longer trains with better fuel economy, less slack action, faster brake response, less stress on mobile equipment (couplers and drawbars) and less wear on track as well, as the DP minimizes the "stringlining" effect where pulling forces on long trains increase the drag on the inside rail of the curve.

The control units/displays are located in the cab, usually atop the control stand. Early systems (through the Locotrol III version) were add-ons; modern versions are integrated to the locomotives' panel computer screens. The engineer can operate the DPUs in synchronous mode, where all locomotives respond to the same commands, or independently. Since radio reception can be intermittent, especially in mountainous areas, modern systems maintain two separate radio transmitter/receiver links. If communication is lost, the DPUs will continue operating at their most-recent setting. As a safeguard, a brake application by the lead locomotives will trigger the remote units to go to idle.

Microprocessor systems allow real-time analysis of data and can provide performance summaries. This is a trip report for a locomotive on a coal train from the mine to the first stop at Bill, Wyo., on Union Pacific.
Trains collection

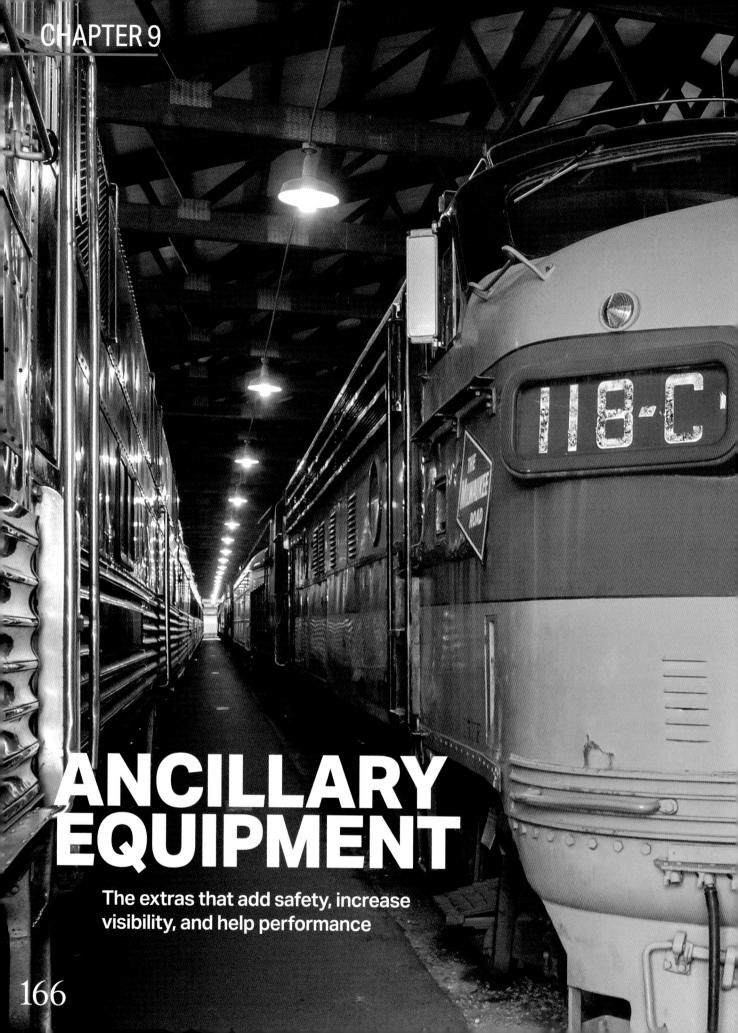

CHAPTER 9

ANCILLARY EQUIPMENT

The extras that add safety, increase visibility, and help performance

This nose view of Milwaukee Road F7 No. 118C shows the locomotive's headlights (single-bulb upper; rotating dual Mars light lower), number boxes with number boards, and class lights (above the number boards). The grab iron atop the side of the nose is designed to hold hooks on a ladder. The locomotive is preserved at the Illinois Railway Museum. *Jeff Wilson*

Along with the engine, generator, and major control components, a variety of other equipment helps diesel-electric locomotives do their jobs safely and efficiently. Many of these items are mandatory (required by operation or safety rules) and some are optional, but much like an automobile that is available with multiple options, specific devices vary by locomotive builder, model, era, and railroad.

As recently as the 1970s, when there were still dozens of Class I railroads, there was a lot of variety in individual locomotive models, as any given model might be purchased by 20, 30, or more railroads. Variations include types of headlights, horns, bells, fuel tank sizes, plows, and other items that served as spotting features for locomotives of various railroads. Since then, mergers have left us with only six Class I railroads. As a result, builders have moved to standardized locomotives and features, with far fewer variations among locomotive orders.

As with other locomotive components discussed throughout this book, locomotive details and fixtures have changed greatly since the days of first-generation details. We'll look at several of these detail items and see how they've evolved through the years.

Headlights

Headlights are a required feature on locomotives; current rules are specific, requiring 200,000 candlepower of light when operating on the road (yard locomotives have a lower requirement). Road locomotives have lights on the rear as well, with the same requirements if that end is leading a train.

The first diesel switchers typically had a single large bulb in a reflector, much like contemporary steam locomotives. This was fine for slow-speed operations, and through the early diesel era, headlights were only turned on at night. Since then, lamps have become brighter. Single bulbs in reflectors remained common in cab units, along with groups of bulbs (up to seven) in a single fixture. By the 1950s, a pair of fixed (sealed-beam) lamps in a single fixture became the common standard, mounted vertically or horizontally. A dimming switch is also required.

With the coming of high-speed diesel-powered streamliners in the 1930s, first with integrated power cars and then separate passenger locomotives, railroads soon realized that something more than standard headlights and horn signals was needed to call attention to trains approaching grade crossings.

The result was the development of moving headlights of various types. The most common were Mars lights (made by Mars; now Tri-Lite, Inc.) and Gyralites, made by Pyle (now Trans-Lite), the other dominant maker of headlights. These moved in various back-and-forth and up-and-down patterns, and were made in single- and double-light versions. They could be mounted in locomotives' standard housings (including upper and lower positions in E, F, and other cab units) or could be in their own housings atop the hood or on the end of a locomotive. They were used in conjunction with standard (sealed-beam, or non-moving) headlights.

Cab units often had headlights both on the top of the nose and in a lower position on the nose door as well; road switchers have headlights either above the cab windows, on the nose, or both. Where both positions are used, one is often a standard fixed headlight, with the other a moving light or an emergency signal (red) light, used by some railroads to indicate that a train has come to an emergency stop.

By the 1960s the most common headlights were twin sealed-beam lamps, which remained on in the daytime for visibility. The latest evolution is light-emitting diode (LED)

headlights. These generally comprise multiple LEDs in a single housing.

Ditch lights

Ditch lights — also called auxiliary or grade-crossing lights — began appearing on Canadian locomotives in the 1970s. They have taken on the role of original motion lights, calling attention to a train approaching a crossing.

Ditch lights became mandatory for locomotives in the U.S. as of Dec. 31, 1997, specifically required for locomotives operating over public grade crossings at speeds greater than 20 mph. They consist of a pair of low-mounted lights, one on each side of the front of the locomotive. They are normally on, and when approaching a grade crossing they flash alternately. Regulations specify their placement (with minimum and maximum height and spacing), but their exact placement varies by locomotive type and railroad. They're mounted on or slightly below or above the anticlimber.

Ancillary details on this Rock Island Electro-Motive SW switcher include footboards on the pilot, a large single-bulb headlight with small number boards on either side, a hood-top bell, and a single-note horn on the front cab wall. *Jeff Wilson collection*

Early diesels in particular featured a wide variety of headlight styles. This Southern Pacific (sublettered for subsidiary Texas & New Orleans) GP9, built in 1957, has a large "barrel-style" Pyle moving light atop the end, with a twin sealed-beam headlight between the number boards/train indicator boards. *EMD*

Class lights

Classification lights were required for locomotives on many routes through the early diesel era, when traffic on most major lines was controlled by dispatchers using timetable and train-order operation. This system identified extra trains (those not listed in the timetable) by having them display a white flag (daytime) or white classification light (night). A green flag and light indicated that there was a following section of a scheduled train.

Class lights on most diesels were in single-lens housings located on either side of the nose on cab units (either in its own housing or as part of the number box) and on either side/corner of the high or low nose on road switchers. Colored lenses rotated into position behind the lens to change colors. Some later Alco road switchers and other locomotives had separate class lights located above the number boards on the front of the cab on either side of the headlights. A red lens was included as well,

for use as a marker light when a locomotive is at the rear of a train (such as operating by itself or in pusher or helper service).

With the demise of timetable/train order operations, older locomotives often have these lights removed with the openings plated over. Many newer locomotives have what at first glance looks like class lights, but they are red lenses only to serve as rear markers.

Beacons

The 1970s saw an increased use of rooftop beacons, usually orange housings with either rotating lamps or a series of four lamps that alternated in pattern to provide a moving effect. Although never required by law, many railroads used them; their main purpose was to make locomotives easier to spot. They were usually placed atop the cab roof, and their size and shape varied by manufacturer.

By the 2000s, railroads using beacons had largely shifted to strobe-style lights (in white housings). Roof-mounted flashing lights are also used on locomotives in remote-control

This Southern Pacific GP9 has a Pyle Gyralite (oscillating) single red light at top, with a twin Pyle Gyralite (white lights) oscillating fixture below that, and twin sealed-beam headlights at bottom.
EMD

Many modern locomotives now have LED headlights, as on Canadian National SD70M-2 No. 8801. The locomotive also has red marker lights (above the windshields) and ditch lights above the anticlimber.
Cody Grivno

operation (controlled by an operator on the ground), to indicate communication status with the controller.

Number boards and boxes

The front of cab-unit and road switcher locomotives, the rear of most road switchers, and both ends of switchers have illuminated number boards at each corner. Styles vary widely, with manufacturers having their own designs and individual railroads adopting designs as well. The "number board" is the actual plate showing the number; a "number box" is the larger housing that holds the board (and usually contains a lighting fixture behind the board).

Most railroads have historically used these to display locomotive numbers, but some railroads (notably Southern Pacific and Union Pacific) through the 1960s used them to show the train number, calling them "train indicator boards."

Horns and bells

Horns and bells are required equipment on a locomotive, and are needed for warnings as well as signaling. The steam whistle was an iconic element of railroading, and many regard the air horn as a decidedly inferior device. The key difference is that a true whistle requires a much higher volume of air (as steam, readily available from a

steam locomotive's boiler), to pass across an opening to create the sound.

A horn works differently. It relies on lower pressure (about 140 pounds), using air from the same compressor and supply as the brake system. Instead of passing across an opening, the air creates a vibration of a reed or diaphragm. The tubular shape of the horn (called the "bell") amplifies the sound and projects it in one direction.

Many early locomotive horns were one-bell (single-note) versions, often applied in pairs with one facing each direction. Horn manufacturers (Nathan and Leslie have long been the primary suppliers) soon began to improve the sound by grouping three or five bells together and tuning them to specific musical chords. Variations include

Ditch lights, common in Canada since the 1970s, became mandatory in the U.S. in 1997. They were added to older locomotives, including this Wisconsin & Southern SD40-2. It's mounted above the anticlimber, next to the multiple-unit cable receptacle.
Cody Grivno

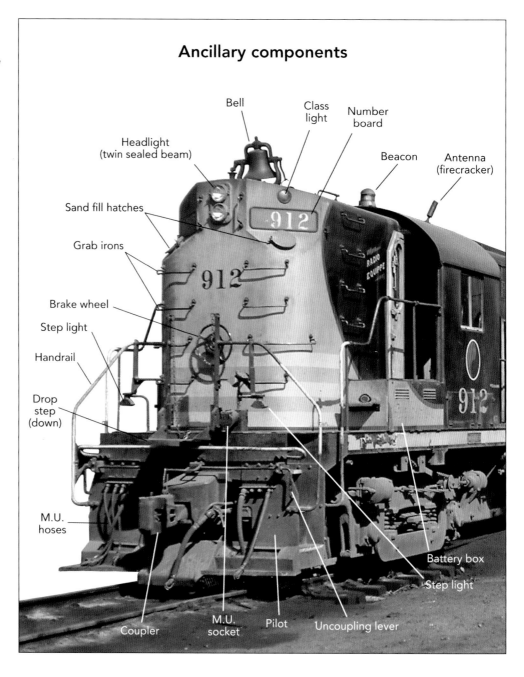

Ancillary components

Bell

Class light

Number board

Headlight (twin sealed beam)

Beacon

Antenna (firecracker)

Sand fill hatches

Grab irons

Brake wheel

Step light

Handrail

Drop step (down)

M.U. hoses

Battery box

Step light

Coupler

M.U. socket

Pilot

Uncoupling lever

the chords as well as the bell direction — many multi-chime horns have one or two bells reversed to provide coverage in both directions. Railroads tended to adopt certain brands and styles of horns as standard, making them a distinct spotting (and sounding) feature.

A notable variation used by some railroads in the 1950s and 1960s was the Hancock air whistle (the New Haven was

the major user). Hancock had been a major supplier of steam whistles for locomotives, and the air whistle was an attempt to capture a sound more like a steam whistle. It can be easily spotted by its tubular shape with a reflector dish at the base to project the sound forward.

Horn placement varies, with each railroad adopting its own practices. Most early cab units had a pair of single-note horns directly

The beacon on this Santa Fe FP45 is on a small platform at the angle of the cab roof. Behind it is the cab air conditioner. The round fixtures on the nose are sand filler hatches. *Ken Koehler*

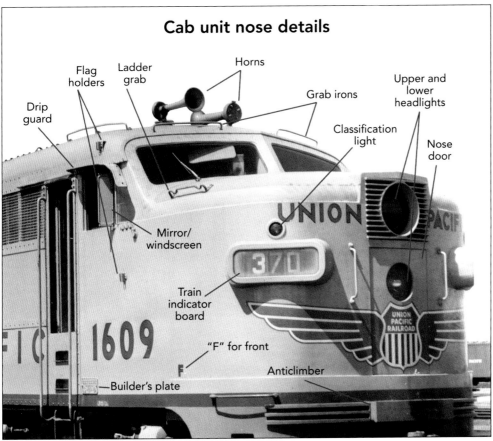

Cab unit nose details

Drip guard
Flag holders
Ladder grab
Horns
Grab irons
Upper and lower headlights
Classification light
Nose door
Mirror/windscreen
Train indicator board
1609
"F" for front
Anticlimber
Builder's plate
370

The Union Pacific was among railroads that used number boards to show train numbers. This Alco FA1 in 1962 is heading train 370, a mixed train from Denver to Ellis, Kan. Flag holders were used to carry flags indicating train status (white for extra; green indicating following sections of the same train). *Louis A. Marre*

above the cab, one facing each direction. On hood units, multi-chime horns became more common. Horns are often atop the cab, but this makes for a loud environment for crews. Alternate locations are on the top of the hood toward the rear or on the side of the hood.

Bells are another safety device, with use mandated in specific situations by the rulebook. Most diesels use conventional bell styles as used on steam locomotives, with the ringer mechanism automated and controlled by air (with an on/off switch on the engineer's control stand).

On cab units, typical bell location is just behind the pilot, largely hidden from view. Some road switchers and switchers have the

The Chicago & North Western favored gong-style bells placed on the noses of many of its hood units. The horn on this SD40-2 is a three-chime model (with the middle bell aimed rearward), and the locomotive has a twin sealed-beam light fixture above the cab windows. *J. David Ingles*

The device to the left of the headlight on this Conrail SW1200 is a Hancock air whistle. The locomotive was originally built for the New Haven, a railroad that favored air whistles instead of standard horns. *Scott A. Hartley*

bell located atop or along the hood or atop the front of the cab; many have it mounted to the underframe near the fuel tank or behind the pilot.

A variation is the "gong" style bell. This dish-shaped bell with internal clapper was favored mainly by the Chicago & North Western, which often located it on the low nose of road switchers.

Antennas

The introduction of mobile radio communications starting in the 1940s required antennas. Through the 1970s this usually meant a single antenna atop the cab roof, but the coming of additional radio devices required multiple antennas. These included remote control of helper and distributed power unit (DPU) locomotives (starting in the 1970s), end-of-train (EOT) devices (1970s), Wi-Fi (2000s), cellular phones (2000s), and GPS for positive train control (2010s).

Conventional radios were marked by antennas of various styles, including the

"wagon wheel" (circular spoked fixture on a vertical post), firecracker (a vertical cylinder atop a thin post, resembling an inverted firecracker), can (a cylinder that looked like an inverted coffee can), and Sinclair (horizontal bar resembling an inverted skate blade). Each type and size of antenna has different properties, making them suitable for various purposes.

Specific antenna locations (and types) vary. They're usually located atop the cab, sometimes mounted directly to the roof and sometimes on a separate horizontal steel plate mounted to the roof. On modern locomotives, antenna groups (or individual antennas) are often covered by a large white or translucent dome.

A distinctive early antenna was required by the Pennsylvania Railroad's Trainphone system. Technically an induction (not radio) system, it relied on large roof-mounted antennas that looked like long handrails with multiple stanchions. These were used by the PRR from the mid-1940s into the 1960s.

Pilots, couplers, plows

The pilot serves multiple purposes. The front surface extends down near rail height and protects the locomotive by deflecting any stray objects on the track before they can pass under the locomotive and cause damage or derailments. The pilot can be flat or angled (to better deflect obstructions); cab-unit pilots were rounded. The pilot also serves as the mounting location for other accessories.

The anticlimber is the horizontal protrusion just above the pilot (below the walkway on road switchers). As the name implies, it helps keep any objects that are struck by the locomotive (for example, a vehicle in a grade-crossing accident) from rising above the pilot, potentially damaging the cab and injuring the crew.

Switching locomotives (and many road switchers) once had footboards on their pilots. A carry-over from steam days, a footboard is a

Modern locomotives have a wide array of antennas, such as the multiple Sinclair antennas on this Union Pacific ES44AC. Smaller antennas are sometimes under opaque housings.
Ken Fitzgerald

On some modern loco-motives, the entire antenna cluster (or individual antennas) is covered by an opaque dome. This is BNSF ES44C4 No. 6756 in 2014. *Cody Grivno*

narrow platform allowing a switchman to ride on the front of the locomotive, just above the rail. The practice was dangerous, and many railroads banned their employees from riding on footboards long before the device itself was banned in 1979.

Many locomotives operating in northern climates are equipped with permanently mounted snow plows. These come in many styles and shapes, and include openings for couplers and air hoses.

Knuckle couplers are standard on all locomotives. The current version is the Type E, in use since the start of the diesel era. The couplers and draft gear are mounted in boxes at the ends of the frame, giving them strength to deal with buffing forces of the train. The coupler head is the C-shaped solid main portion; the knuckle is the pivoting piece that opens to allow coupling and closes to lock together with the adjoining coupler. The shank or drawbar extends rearward and is secured to the frame, while allowing slight side to side movement. The box and connectors together form the draft gear, which also includes rubber pads for cushioning.

An uncoupling lever extends from the coupler and is mounted to both sides of the pilot, enabling a crew member to open the knuckle by pulling upward on the lever.

Various air hoses are also mounted on the pilot; their functions are described in Chapters 4 and 7.

The rooftop antennas for the Pennsylvania Railroad's Trainphone system were prominent — they look like long handrails. This is a new F3 built in 1948. *EMD*

Many locomotives are equipped with pilot-mounted snowplows, including this BNSF Dash 8-40BW. Also note the ditch lights mounted below the anticlimber. *Cody Grivno*

Handrails, grab irons, steps, cab exteriors

The placement of handrails, grab irons, and steps is tightly regulated, with their specific locations (as well as colors) spelled out by rules. Grab irons are short horizontal or vertical railings mounted to the body; they are often stacked to serve as steps. On cab units, this means vertical grabs above steps leading to cab and engine-room doors, above and along windshields, on the roof, and on the rear above the pilot. Horizontal grabs often form a ladder up one side of the nose (and across the nose) as well. Hood units also have grabs forming steps to the roof at the rear.

Steps extending below the frame are found at the corners of road switchers and directly below doors on cab units. These can be stirrup-style (cab units) or deeper steps (hoods), but safety rules require crew to treat them as ladders, since their pitch is steep.

Longer handrails, supported by vertical posts (stanchions) are used along running

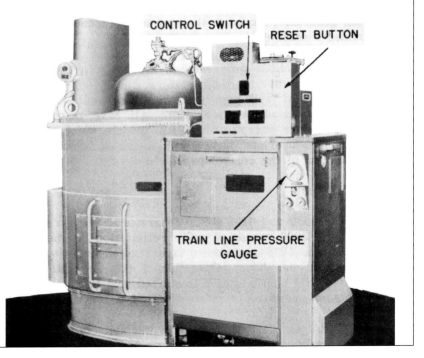

Steam generators are diesel-fired. Water, run through coils, is heated by flame to make steam. They came in several sizes: This is a Vapor-Clarkson model 4630 generator with a capacity of 3,000 pounds per hour. *EMD*

CONTROL SWITCH

RESET BUTTON

TRAIN LINE PRESSURE GAUGE

This EMD E8 has a pair of steam generators at the rear, marked by pairs of vents and exhaust stacks on the rear-most roof hatch. The boxy housing on the next panel is a winterization hatch covering a pair of radiator fans. *EMD*

The rear access doors on this Seaboard Air Line SDP35 are open, revealing the steam generator. The EMD SDP35 was an SD35 road switcher equipped for passenger service, geared for high speed. It was a 1960s solution to railroads in need of passenger diesels. *EMD*

boards (walkways) along the sides of road switchers, as well as on the outside of the end platforms, where they angle downward at the corners to serve as step railings.

Locomotives often have additional ladder grab irons on the nose and roof. These are designed for maintenance crews using a separate ladder with top hooks that attach to the grabs, securing them firmly.

Most road switchers have a gap in the railing at each end platform to allow crew members to cross between locomotives. These have drop steps that lower into place, with safety chains that connect between locomotives on either side of the drop step.

The SDP40F was the first diesel bought new by Amtrak, with the first arriving in 1973. The cowl-style locomotive had two steam generators at the rear of the hood, marked by stacks and vents.
John H. Kuehl

Cabs also have a variety of external features, including side mirrors, wind deflectors, retractable sunshades, drip rails, and windshield wipers. The side windows generally slide open. Air conditioners were rare on early diesels but became more common from the 1960s onward, and generally are a boxy housing on the cab roof.

Steam generators

Well into the diesel era, passenger trains were heated and cooled by steam, provided via a steam line (pipe) that ran throughout the train. With steam locomotives, this source of steam was readily available. The coming of diesel streamliners in the mid-1930s required a new method of supplying steam: the self-contained steam generator.

Not all locomotives had steam generators. All early dedicated passenger locomotives (Es, PAs) did, as did dual-service freight/passenger locomotives. Most railroads had a few freight cab units and road switchers equipped with steam generators either for part-time (or backup) passenger duty or for service on branch lines and locals.

Steam was carried throughout the train by a steam line, with a pipe connection at the end of the locomotive and on each car. The valve is cracked open on the pilot of this New Haven EMD FL9, with steam escaping on a February day in 1986.
Scott A. Hartley

Looking like a small furnace, the steam generator is located at the rear of cab-style diesels and most low-nose road switchers, and in the tall noses of early passenger-service road switchers (Alco RS and EMD GP and SD designs). The generator gets its water from a tank located either below the frame adjacent to the fuel tank, under the cab, or in the engine compartment (some locomotives had multiple tanks). It's powered by the same diesel fuel as the engine. Controls on the

Locomotives have one or two sandboxes (and filler hatches) at each end. Here a Soo Line worker uses a hose from a sanding tower to replenish the traction sand on a U25B demonstrator. *Soo Line*

Sand filler hatches on cab units were typically hinged covers on the sides near the cab and on the rear of the side wall, above the trucks. This a later pull-down-handle style on an F unit; some earlier hatch covers had knobs that had to be turned to open the hatches.
Jeff Wilson

fireman's side of the cab allow turning the generator on and off and regulating the steam production; the generator also has controls mounted directly to it.

Some think of the steam generator as a small boiler, which it is, but not in the conventional design with a tank. Instead, a series of spiral coils move water through the heating chamber, where a diesel-fired flame brings the water quickly to its boiling point.

Steam generators were made in multiple sizes, rated by how much steam they could produce (measured by how many pounds of water they could turn to steam in an hour). The first, in Union Pacific's *City of Portland* streamliner in 1935, had a capacity of 800 pounds per hour. By the 1940s, units could produce 2,000 pounds per hour or more. How they were used varied by train length and season. A long train in the winter might have an additional locomotive or two added not because of horsepower needs, but to ensure an adequate steam supply.

Steam generators gave way to electrical heating and cooling in the 1970s, in the form of head-end power (HEP) units (described in Chapter 4).

Sandbox

Sand for traction is important for operation. Diesel locomotives have one or two internal sandboxes at each end. Older cab units typically had four boxes, one above each side of each truck (with the boxes mounted inside the walls), marked by a small hatch cover on the side. Road switchers have one or two at each end, with a hatch centered atop the nose (or one at each corner) and atop the end of the long hood.

A road locomotive typically has a capacity of 40 to 50 cubic feet of sand (4,000 to 5,000 pounds, as a cubic foot of dry sand weighs about 100 pounds). Pipes carry the sand to each truck sideframe ahead of the lead driving wheel. Air forces the sand through delivery pipes to the rail. A valve on the engineer's control stand turns sanders on and off; automated wheel-slip systems apply sand automatically as needed.

Fuel and water tanks

Chapter 2 describes the fuel system. Many locomotives offered multiple options for fuel tank sizes. On modern locomotives and most older models, the fuel tank is suspended from the underframe between the trucks. Road switchers have the largest tanks, ranging from around 2,100 gallons to 3,500 gallons for most locomotives through the 1970s. Modern diesels have larger tanks, typically 4,000 to 5,600 gallons. Switchers' tanks were smaller, with capacities of 600 to 1,000 gallons; early cab units were slightly larger — 1,200 gallons for EMD E and F units.

Tank shape varies widely by manufacturer, model, and era. Some have vertical side walls (or vertical sides that angle inward at the bottom. Others have rounded

sides that extend outward for increased capacity. Some switchers and early road switchers — Alco's RS2, for example — had a fuel tank above the frame and below the cab. These have a tell-tale fuel filler cap below the cab window on each side.

For passenger locomotives in the era of steam generators, one or more water tanks were needed. This could be an internal tank in the engine compartment (see Chapter 6) or it could be a second tank next to the fuel tank under the underframe. Several designs were used: The water tank was sometimes next to the fuel tank, but on some locomotives the water and fuel tanks nested inside each other, both to save space and provide a layer of protection for the fuel tank (by having the water tank over it). A below-frame water tank usually meant a smaller-than-standard fuel tank; it also often resulted in the air reservoirs being relocated to the roof.

This Milwaukee Road EMD E9 has a combined fuel/water tank (the fuel tank is nested inside the water tank). Fillers are labeled for boiler (steam generator) water and fuel oil, as well as two smaller fillers for engine water (one for each engine).
Trains collection

Alco's RS2 has its fuel tank above the frame and below the cab floor (the filler is just to the right of the Great Northern herald on the cab). Below the frame are the battery boxes and air reservoirs. Also note the separate angled number boards, steam-style classification lights, and the boxy all-weather window on the cab.
Jeff Wilson collection

CHAPTER 10

ELECTRIC LOCOMOTIVES

Electricity offers great power and speed, but the infrastructure poses big challenges

A Siemens Sprinter ACS64 leads an Amtrak train of Amfleet cars under catenary at Princeton Junction, N.J., in August 2019. The AC-motor ACS-64 is a modern 8,600-hp electric locomotive operating on Amtrak's Northeast Corridor.
David Lassen

Electric locomotives, which take their power from an external source (overhead wire or electrified outside third rail), predate diesels. As heavy electric locomotives grew in power and size, their technological advancements in the 1920s and 1930s helped spur the development and evolution of later diesel-electric locomotives.

Streetcars and interurbans

The first electric railways were streetcars and interurban lines. Streetcars, as the name implies, run on streets and private rights-of-way within cities and urban areas. Street railways had been around — albeit horse-powered — since the early 1800s, with the first electric-powered cars appearing in Cleveland in 1884. Many cities soon adopted electric streetcars, and by the 1890s, interurban lines were being built to connect towns and cities. Interurbans were built on a private right-of-way or adjacent to a roadway, and usually connected directly to the streetcar lines in the towns they

served. Interurbans were designed primarily for passenger traffic and, although standard gauge, were built with lighter (and cheaper) materials than steam railroads, with smaller/lighter rail, less roadbed and ballast (or no ballast), steeper grades, and tighter curves.

Streetcars and interurbans were self-propelled cars that were far less powerful than a locomotive on a conventional (steam) railroad. They operated as single cars, but sometimes pulled a trailing coach or a freight car or two.

Early streetcar and interurban systems operated on low voltage (500-600 volts) DC, generally from an overhead wire, with a trolley pole atop the car in contact with the wire via a small roller or shoe. Cars generally resembled passenger cars with an operator's stand at one or both ends. Power was routed through a controller and directly to traction motors that powered the axles. Along with self-propelled passenger cars, interurban lines sometimes used separate small locomotives (often steeple-cab design) to pull the few freight cars or work trains that needed to be handled.

Interurban lines were built to lighter standards than steam railroads. The self-propelled electric cars, with truck-mounted traction motors, led to the development of heavy-electric locomotives. This is along one of the last interurbans, the Illinois Terminal, at Gardena, Ill., in 1953.
Paul Stringham

The technology involved in early streetcars and interurbans, although involving lower power and lighter equipment, provided the groundwork for designing the larger, more-powerful electric locomotives that shortly began appearing on standard railroads.

Heavy electric locomotives

Electrification on portions of mainline railroads with more-powerful locomotives and higher voltage — known as "heavy electric" systems and locomotives — started with a stretch of the Baltimore & Ohio at Baltimore in 1895. Much early electrification was in and near large passenger terminals and/or long tunnels, due to problems with smoke generated by steam locomotives. Other electrification projects were generally along high-traffic passenger lines or in mountainous areas, where high-tonnage trains climbed steep grades through tunnels.

Some significant heavy-electric installations from 1900 through the 1920s included the Pennsylvania Railroad (New York to Washington, D.C.), New York Central (Hudson and Harlem Divisions and Grand Central Terminal), New York, New Haven & Hartford (Woodlawn, N.Y., to New Haven, Conn.), Norfolk & Western (52 miles in West Virginia), Virginian Railway (134 miles), Great Northern (Cascade Mountains, 73 miles), Milwaukee Road (Rocky Mountains, two stretches, 645 miles), and several industrial railroads, notably the Butte, Anaconda & Pacific (Montana, 30 miles).

Electric locomotives have many positive attributes. Because they have full electrical power available to them at all times from the overhead wire (no waiting for an engine and generator to reach speed), they have outstanding acceleration, and are more powerful, with higher tractive effort and horsepower than comparable diesel-electrics. Electric locomotives have historically been durable and long-lasting, as they don't have the maintenance of the diesel prime mover. Electrics are also more efficient, with a central generating plant producing electricity instead of dozens (or hundreds) of multiple small portable engines. Electrics can use any type of generating source, including wind, solar, or hydroelectric.

The biggest issue of electric installations, and the main reason most early heavy electric lines were eventually retired and few new ones have been built, isn't the locomotives, but the infrastructure required. Installing catenary wire costs millions of dollars per mile

Two Sacramento Northern steeple-cab freight motors have just brought their train down a 4% grade and are pausing to let wheels and brake shoes cool. The SN was a heavy interurban line (using 600 to 1,500 volts DC) that carried significant freight; this scene is from 1945.
Arthur Lloyd, Jr.

Early heavy electric locomotives often had steam locomotive-style running gear. Great Northern's GE-built Y-1 locomotives had a 1-C+C-1 arrangement, with single-axle lead and trailing trucks and two three-axle sets of driving wheels. The 3,000-hp locomotives served on GN's 11,000-volt AC system in the Cascade Mountains. *General Electric*

Opposite page: General Electric's GEA-625A traction motor (shown with covers removed in this 1931 view) is a geared quill drive, with two motors powering one axle (which will pass through the hole at bottom). Each motor is rated at 385 hp, for 770 hp per axle. It was used on the GG1 and other electric locomotives. *General Electric*

and requires regular maintenance, and the significantly higher clearances involved mean bridges, tunnels, and other infrastructure must be modified or rebuilt.

This is why the stretches that remain in service in the U.S. are high-volume lines, namely the Northeast Corridor and related lines at large passenger terminals, while most electric freight installations were removed from the 1950s through the 1970s.

Electric system basics

Early heavy electric locomotives were far more powerful than streetcars and interurbans — 2,000 hp and higher. Two builders initially dominated the market: Westinghouse, usually in partnership with Baldwin, and General Electric, which often partnered with Alco. Westinghouse and GE were also heavily involved in designing electric railroad infrastructure as well (catenary, generating equipment, etc.).

Electric locomotives' increased size and power compared to streetcar systems required more current to operate. Although some systems continued to use DC, but at a higher voltage (notably Milwaukee Road's 3,000-volt DC installation), most railroads opted for higher-voltage (11,000-volt), single-phase AC. The higher voltage meant lower current, and AC can travel longer distances in transmission lines with lower voltage drop compared to DC.

Early electric locomotive design was heavily influenced by steam locomotive practices for frames and running gear. Many had unpowered lead and trailing trucks, with three to eight driving axles in a large cast (rigid) frame in the middle. Locomotives were usually articulated if they had more than four driving axles, with one or two traction motors on each axle. The photo on the next page shows this, with the driving-axle frames connected at an articulation joint between them.

These early electrics also had larger driving wheels than later diesel-electrics. The Pennsylvania Railroad's GG1 locomotives, for example, had 36-inch wheels on its unpowered leading and trailing trucks, but 57-inch driving wheels: compare this with the 40- to 42-inch wheels on most modern diesel-electrics. Wheel arrangements are figured in the same method as diesels, with unpowered axles indicated by numbers and powered axles by letters. Thus the GG1 (four-wheel pilot and trailing trucks, with six powered axles in two articulated sets) had a wheel arrangement of 2-C+C-2, which in Pennsylvania Railroad terminology roughly translates to two 4-6-0 steam locomotives coupled back-to-back.

Traction motors on these locomotives were mounted to the frame and geared to axles. Through the 1930s many electrics were built with twin motors on each axle, using what is known as a quill drive. This

allows the two motor pinion gears to mesh with a single axle-mounted gear. Some early heavy electrics used large motors not mounted to an axle. These were connected by rods to one driving axle, with side rods connecting other drivers (see the Virginian boxcab on page 188).

By the 1950s, new electric locomotives generally rode on separate trucks, which were equipped with traction motors in the same method as diesel-electrics.

Bodies on early heavy electrics were typically boxcab designs, often with cabs at both ends. By the late 1930s, these were giving way to streamlined designs with noses or central cabs with long, tapered prows fore and aft, looking more like diesel streamliners. By the 1950s designs moved to road-switcher or fully-enclosed cowl-style bodies.

Early electric locomotives were the first to feature multiple-unit (m.u.) connections, allowing two locomotives to be controlled from a single point, and many electrics were designed specifically to be used in sets of two or three.

Drive and power systems

With no diesel engine, what takes up the space inside an electric locomotive

This view of New Haven streamlined EP-4 electrics under construction at General Electric in 1938 shows the cast frames with twin quill-drive traction motors on each driving axle. The articulation pivot joint is visible between the two three-axle frames; the locomotives have four-wheel lead and pilot trucks.
General Electric

Virginian's EL-3a boxcab electric locomotives had two large Westinghouse 452A induction motors that each powered two driving axles (62" driving wheels) via side rods. Built in 1925 by Westinghouse/Alco, they typically operated in sets of three (7,125 total peak hp). *Alco*

body? The specifics depend upon the control system, voltage, and traction motors (mounting system and whether they're AC or DC). A key component is a large, oil-cooled transformer, which steps down the high voltage from the overhead wire to lower voltage to allow it to be used by the control system. Multiple heavy circuit breakers, relays, and switches protect and control the various electrical circuits.

On DC-power systems, the voltage is stepped down and routed by the control system to the traction motors themselves,

much the same way power is routed from the generator to the motors on a diesel-electric locomotive. A notable variation is the bipolar motor, used most famously on Milwaukee Road's EP-2 locomotives, built in 1918 (and usually known simply as bipolars). These had steam-style articulated frames for the large driving wheels (two sets of four axles), with the traction motor bodies mounted to the frame. What made them unique was that the motors were essentially built around the axles, with the armature mounted directly on the driving axle. This way the motor directly

By the 1950s, electric locomotives usually followed the same body styles as diesel-electrics, with road-switcher bodies atop conventional trucks. This Virginian EL-C locomotive, built by GE, uses ignitron rectifiers to convert AC to DC. The 3,300-hp locomotive was built in 1955. *General Electric*

The cab of this seven-year-old Virginian EL-C electric looks a lot like a typical diesel-electric road-switcher cab of the 1950s, but with more electrical gauges on the control stand. The large sweep controller is directly in front of the engineer's seat, with the brake stand at left. *J. Parker Lamb*

turned the axle, eliminating the need for motor-to-axle gearing.

For AC-overhead-wire systems, the process is more complex. Some locomotives used AC traction motors wired in series. Speed control was limited, and was accomplished by switching the output of the taps of the locomotive's transformers.

An option on AC systems through the 1940s was a motor-generator drive. On these locomotives (such as the Great Northern Y-1)), the high-voltage AC is stepped down via a transformer, then the resulting lower-voltage power drives a synchronous AC motor (in which the rotational speed is tied to the frequency of the electricity). The motor in turn drives a generator, which produces DC for the traction motors. Since motor/generator speed is constant, speed control is accomplished by varying the amount of excitation provided to the generator fields.

The motor-generator sets worked well, but took up considerable space under the hood. Some locomotives used a single motor with one or two generators; some larger locomotives used two motors, with one or two generators on each motor. The motor-generators, with their moving parts, could also be maintenance intensive.

It takes a transformer of significant size to step down the power from the high-voltage overhead wire to the control system. This air- and oil-cooled transformer is being prepped for installation in a Pennsylvania Railroad GG1 in the 1930s. *General Electric*

Most electric locomotives feature regenerative braking. This is explained in Chapter 4, and is similar to dynamic braking in a diesel-electric. When the traction motors are turned into generators, the electricity generated is routed back into the overhead wire, where it can be used by other locomotives on the system. The amount of braking is regulated by varying the excitation applied to the motors.

On many modern electrics, these have been replaced by conventional dynamic brakes, and some passenger locomotives have "blended

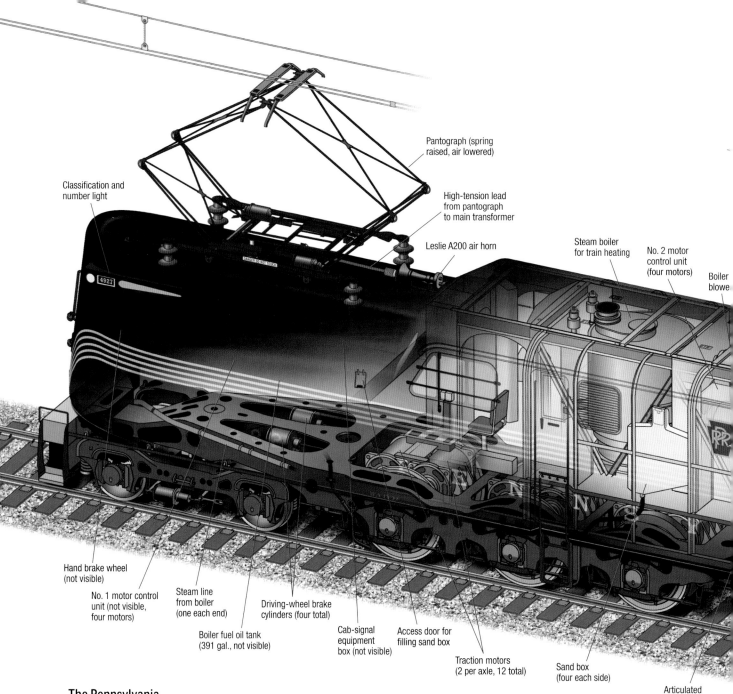

Pantograph (spring raised, air lowered)

High-tension lead from pantograph to main transformer

Classification and number light

Leslie A200 air horn

Steam boiler for train heating

No. 2 motor control unit (four motors)

Boiler blowe

Hand brake wheel (not visible)

No. 1 motor control unit (not visible, four motors)

Steam line from boiler (one each end)

Driving-wheel brake cylinders (four total)

Boiler fuel oil tank (391 gal., not visible)

Cab-signal equipment box (not visible)

Access door for filling sand box

Traction motors (2 per axle, 12 total)

Sand box (four each side)

Articulated connection

The Pennsylvania Railroad's GG1 is among the best-known electric locomotives. First built in 1934, some in the class served into the 1980s. This view shows its major components.
Kalmbach Media

brakes," which apply the air and dynamic brakes simultaneously, while allowing dynamic braking to help provide HEP power.

Rectifiers

In the mid-1950s, locomotive builders applied new technology to convert the AC line power to DC for the traction motors using ignitron rectifiers. The first were General Electric's designs for Virginian class EL-C (later to New Haven as EF-4 and

E33) and later Pennsylvania Railroad class E44 locomotives. They were often simply known as "rectifiers."

An ignitron rectifier is a large, gas-filled device (a type of mercury-arc rectifier) that uses an arc that's ignited to allow high current flow between the cathode and anode. They were specifically designed to convert high-voltage, high-current AC to DC in industrial applications, and applying them to locomotives allowed elimination of the motor/generator and all of the moving parts (and related maintenance) of them. Multiple ignitron rectifiers were used: the 4,400-hp E44, for example, used 12 rectifiers.

By the early 1960s, the improvement in solid-state electronic gear led to the transition from arc devices to large banks of silicon-diode rectifiers, starting with the final E44s delivered to Pennsylvania Railroad in 1963. These still required cooling, but were reliable, more compact, and more efficient than the ignitrons. They were the basic technology adapted a few years later for the use of alternators on diesel-electric locomotives.

Another advancement came in the 1970s, with the use of rectifiers and thyristors (controllable rectifiers) to "chop" current

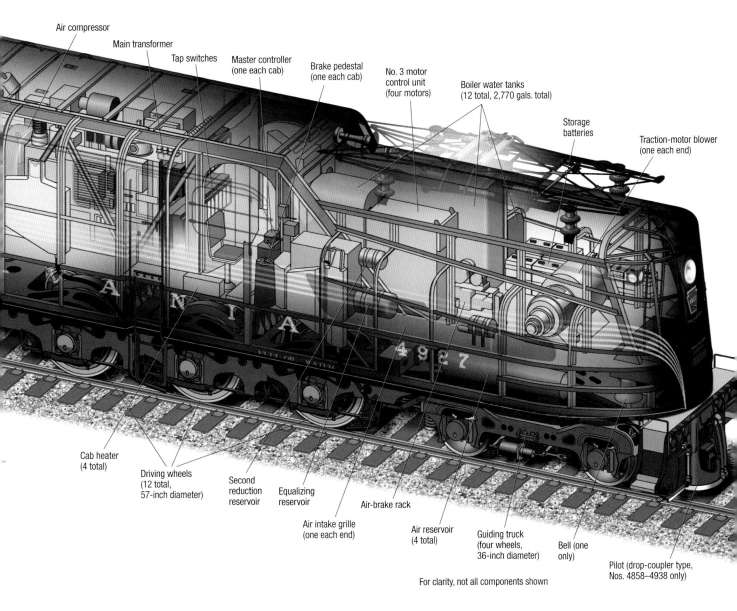

Air compressor

Main transformer

Tap switches

Master controller
(one each cab)

Brake pedestal
(one each cab)

No. 3 motor
control unit
(four motors)

Boiler water tanks
(12 total, 2,770 gals. total)

Storage
batteries

Traction-motor blower
(one each end)

Cab heater
(4 total)

Driving wheels
(12 total,
57-inch diameter)

Second
reduction
reservoir

Equalizing
reservoir

Air intake grille
(one each end)

Air-brake rack

Air reservoir
(4 total)

Guiding truck
(four wheels,
36-inch diameter)

Bell (one
only)

Pilot (drop-coupler type,
Nos. 4858–4938 only)

For clarity, not all components shown

A Milwaukee Road class EP-2 bipolar electric, built in 1918, pulls the *Olympian* in the Cascade Mountains. The EP-2 drive system had the motor armature mounted directly to the axle, eliminating the need for gearing. *Milwaukee Road*

Through the 1940s, many electric locomotives used motor/generator sets. After a transformer stepped down the catenary voltage, the power was used to turn a motor (left end) which turned a generator (right end) which provided power to the traction motors. *General Electric*

going to motors. The first were in Amtrak's AEM-7 locomotives, built starting in 1978 by EMD (with Swedish company ASEA). They were built with DC traction motors, but 29 (of 65) were rebuilt with AC motors starting in 1999.

Modern electric locomotives have adopted AC traction motors. The 8,600-hp Siemens ACS-64, for example, uses a power converter to change AC to DC, then inverters to convert it back to AC to chop the power and feed it to the three-phase

In the 1950s, electric locomotives began using ignitron rectifiers (the large vertical cylinders) to convert overhead-wire AC to DC for traction, replacing motor/generator drive systems. *General Electric*

Amtrak's EMD AEM7 locomotives were built beginning in 1978. The 7,000-hp, 125-mph locomotives were the first to use thyristors for power control, and they were a primary passenger locomotive for Amtrak in the Northeast from the late 1970s into the 2010s.
EMD

AC traction motors. Insulated-gate bipolar transistors (IGBTs) have replaced thyristors.

Ancillary equipment

All of this electrical gear produces a substantial amount of heat, so electric locomotives have extensive blower/cooling systems for various components, along with blowers for the traction motors themselves. And, because electric locomotives are much quieter in operation than a diesel, much of the sound heard while locomotives are active are a locomotive's fans and blowers, along with — especially on older locomotives — the sounds of high-voltage switches and relays being thrown and activated.

To get power from the overhead wire (catenary), electric locomotives use a pantograph, a spring-loaded bracket that presses a pair of transverse sliding pans (pan heads) upward into contact with the wire. A collapsible frame comprising upper and lower arms is pneumatically activated to raise and lower the pantograph. These can be double- or single-armed. The entire assembly is mounted atop insulators, with a cable connection from the pantograph to the transformer inside the locomotive. Most locomotives have two pantographs, one fore and one aft.

Once the pantograph has been raised into position, springs provide upward pressure to maintain contact with the wire as the train is in motion. The wire varies in height, and the wire also has some side-to-side variation

in a regular pattern to distribute wear across the locomotive's pan. The contact surface of the pan is coated in graphite, which is conductive and provides lubrication as well.

Some electric railroads and locomotives use a ground-level third-rail to provide power (particularly in urban areas around large passenger terminals). On these, a spring-loaded shoe mounted on a truck sideframe picks up the power. These can be in a variety of designs. Shoes are located on both sides of a locomotive, as third-rail

Electric locomotives operating in third-rail territory have pickup shoes mounted on a truck sideframe. This is the sprung/retractable shoe on an EMD FL9 dual-power locomotive.
EMD

193

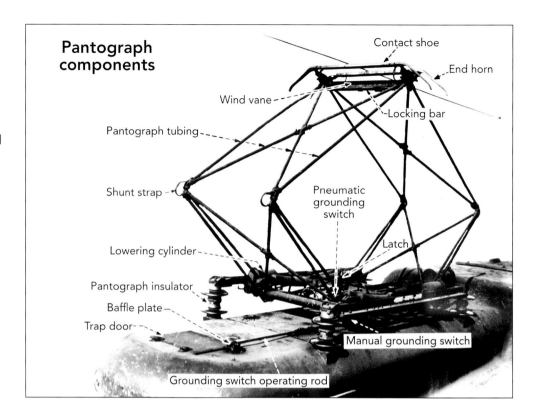

Pantograph components

Contact shoe

End horn

Wind vane

Locking bar

Pantograph tubing

Pneumatic grounding switch

Shunt strap

Latch

Lowering cylinder

Pantograph insulator

Baffle plate

Trap door

Manual grounding switch

Grounding switch operating rod

These are the main components of a pantograph on a Pennsylvania Railroad GG1; those on other locomotives have similar construction. *Pennsylvania Railroad*

location varies depending upon surrounding obstacles and trackwork (such as around turnouts, switch stands, and rail and highway grade crossings).

Passenger electric locomotives into the 1970s were also equipped with steam generators. These are diesel-fuel-fired, so require storage tanks for both fuel and water, with filler hatches on each side of the locomotive (this is why some electrics have a filler with a seemingly ironic "diesel fuel" label). Since the 1970s, this has shifted to head-end power, which doesn't require a separate engine/generator set as on diesel-electrics.

Electric locomotives have large banks of batteries, just like diesel-electrics. They are used by the control system when power is not available from the overhead wire.

Cab and control

Early boxcab electrics were often double-ended, with full cabs and control stands at each end. Other designs had central cabs (Pennsy's GG1 and P5, Milwaukee's bipolars). These had two control stands, one on each side of the cab, to allow bi-directional operation. Most later electrics had conventional cabs, either in cab-unit or road-switcher style.

The EMD FL9 was the first dual-power (diesel-electric/electric) loco-motive, with a third-rail shoe mounted on the lead truck. The New Haven bought 60 in 1956 and 1960; they were the last F units built. *Jim Shaughnessy*

The engineer's cab of the Siemens ACS-64 Sprinter is console style, with the brake stand at right and controller at left. The positive train control (PTC) panel is directly behind the red automatic brake handle; the other screens show operating and system data. *Shane McLeod*

Running an electric locomotive is similar to operating a diesel-electric. The air brake controls are the same. In place of the throttle lever is the "controller," and most provide broader control — the GG1, for example, had a 21-point controller. There's an ammeter showing the load on traction motors and gauges showing the amount of electrical braking, with warning lights applying to the electrical gear (overloads and overheating) instead of engine (oil, radiator, etc.) systems.

Dual-power locomotives

The dual-power (electric/diesel-electric) locomotive was developed at the request of the New York, New Haven & Hartford. The railroad wanted a locomotive that could operate into Grand Central and Penn Station in New York City (on the required third-rail electric system) and also run through to the railroad's non-electrified territory.

The first of these were the last F units built, EMD's FL9, delivered to New Haven in 1956 and 1960 (60 total locomotives). They were mechanically F9s with passenger gearing, a longer body (to hold the added electrical gear), six-wheel rear trucks (A1A) to carry the added weight, and retractable third-rail shoes mounted on their Flexicoil front trucks.

Newer dual-power locomotives include the GE P32AC-DM, built in 1995, and the EMD DM30AC (1997), both of which use third-rail shoes, and the Bombardier ALP45-DP (2008), which uses a pantograph.

The Bombardier ALP45-DP is a modern high-speed, dual-power (diesel-electric/electric with pantograph) locomotive, first built in 2008. New Jersey Transit No. 4501 is under wire at Princeton Junction, N.J.
Brian Solomon

CHAPTER 11

LOCOMOTIVE MANUFACTURERS

Many tried to compete in the diesel-electric marketplace, but two became the dominant force in the field

General Electric ES44AC locomotives of BNSF and Canadian National lead a train in April 2021. The modern 4,400-hp, AC-traction-motor locomotive proved extremely popular, with more than 5,000 built for all North American Class I railroads starting in 2003.
Cody Grivno .

Diesel-electric locomotive manufacturing was dominated by Electro-Motive from the 1930s into the 1980s, with Alco (into the 1960s) and General Electric (1960s and 1970s) bringing up a distant second place. The late 1970s saw a shift in the market, with GE's products growing in sales and then surpassing EMD from 1987 onward.

The Alco PA is one of the all-time favorite diesel locomotives among railfans and modelers. Santa Fe PA1 No. 62 leads Train No. 12 at Lawrence, Kan., in March 1950.
Robert P. Olmsted

Wabtec (the former General Electric) remains the dominant builder as of 2023, with Electro-Motive Diesel — the current iteration (owned by Progress Rail) of the original Electro-Motive Division — trailing. Other builders have also emerged, especially in the specialty passenger market, with Bombardier and Siemens capturing significant sales.

Here, in alphabetical order, are summary histories of the major companies that have produced diesel-electric road locomotives since the 1930s. Chapter 3 included details on each company's diesel engine designs.

American Locomotive Co. (Alco) Montreal Locomotive Works (MLW) Bombardier

The American Locomotive Company (Alco) was the country's second-largest steam locomotive builder behind Baldwin Locomotive Works. It was formed in 1901 with the merger of several smaller builders; it was officially renamed Alco Products in 1955. Its main plant was at Schenectady, N.Y.

Alco was an early builder of electric and internal-combustion locomotives, and in the 1920s, Alco partnered with General Electric and Ingersoll-Rand to build a line of 60- and 100-ton boxcab diesel-electric switchers. Alco began building conventional-design, end-cab switchers on its own in the 1930s, and in 1940 entered a marketing and production partnership for road diesels with GE that would last until 1953.

Notable early diesels from Alco include its DL-series twin-engine passenger units of the 1930s and early 1940s, its better received single-engine PA passenger locomotives built from the mid-1940s into the early 1950s, and RS-series road switchers (including the first true road switcher, the RS-1 of 1941). The company later offered an upgraded line, the Century series of four- and six-axle road switchers, in the 1960s.

Although Alco was the second-largest diesel locomotive builder through the 1950s (and briefly led diesel sales in the mid-1930s), sales of Alco road diesels always trailed those of Electro-Motive. Alco's North American market share (26% in 1946) fell throughout the 1950s. Former partner GE entered the domestic road-switcher market with its U25B in 1959, with sales of its innovative locomotives soon eclipsing Alco's revamped Century line.

Alco's switchers had good reputations, but the performance and reliability of its model 244 diesel engine on road diesels suffered from the 1940s into the 1950s. The company's new 251 engine improved reliability, but it proved too late to save sales. Alco ceased locomotive manufacturing in 1969.

Canadian builder Montreal Locomotive Works (MLW), which had built locomotives under license to Alco (primarily for Canadian railroads), acquired Alco's design patents and continued building its own locomotives. Bombardier acquired a major interest in MLW in 1975, eventually merging MLW. Bombardier continued building diesel-electric locomotives until 1985.

Bombardier, which had continued building light-rail electric locomotives and train sets, re-entered the North American electric locomotive market in the 1990s with its HHP8. Current production models include the electric ALP46 and dual-power (electric/diesel-electric) ALP45-DP (see page 195 in Chapter 10).

Baldwin Locomotive Works

Baldwin was the largest, longest-lived, and most successful steam locomotive builder, producing its first locomotive in 1832. The company finished its move to its plant in Eddystone, Pa. (near Philadelphia), in 1928. Early ventures outside of steam included Depression-era purchases of Whitcomb Locomotive Works (Rochelle, Ill.) and Milwaukee (Wis.) Locomotive Manufacturing Co., both builders of small gasoline and diesel industrial locomotives.

Alco tried various innovations to reclaim its lost market share with its Century-series locomotives in the 1960s, but to no avail. Burlington Northern No. 4363 is a former Spokane, Portland & Seattle 3,600-hp C-636 built in 1967. The large housing behind the cab is the aftercooler.
Jerrold F. Hilton

199

Montreal Locomotive Works continued building Alco-design locomotives after Alco's exit from the market in 1969. This is a 3,000-hp MLW M630 built for Canadian Pacific in February 1970.
Trains collection

Baldwin built heavy electric locomotives in partnership with Westinghouse starting in 1895. (Westinghouse would later supply electrical components for several diesel-electric builders.) However, Baldwin's emphasis remained on steam, and the company continued pushing the older technology while others were focusing on diesels in the 1940s. Baldwin built its last domestic steam locomotives in 1949.

Baldwin began producing diesel switchers in the late 1930s, but other than a few demonstrators didn't start building road diesels until 1945 — several years after EMD and Alco. The company's late start

did not inspire sales, not even to railroads that had been major customers for Baldwin steam locomotives. With its diesel sales declining and rival EMD's market share increasing (Baldwin's diesel market share never exceeded 13%), Baldwin merged with Lima-Hamilton in 1950. But by that time, the market simply couldn't support another diesel manufacturer.

Notable diesels from Baldwin included its VO- and S- series switchers and its distinctive cab units with angled noses, dubbed "sharknose" diesels by railfans. Baldwin diesels had a reputation for being good low-speed lugging locomotives, but

Although poor sellers, Baldwin's shark-nose cab units became an icon for the company. These are 1,600-hp, four-axle RF16 freight A and B units on New York Central.
Louis A. Marre

they suffered from a variety of engine and mechanical issues, and the company could never generate enough sales to fine-tune its products.

Following the Baldwin-Lima-Hamilton merger, the Lima-Hamilton line of switchers and road switchers was discontinued, and the company focused its attention on Baldwin's models. However, the company's sales continued to decline, and Baldwin built its last diesel locomotive in 1956 — just seven years after building its last steam locomotive.

Brookville

Brookville, established in 1918 as Brookville Locomotive Works, has a long history of building small industrial locomotives and heavy equipment (rail and non-rail) for the mining industry. The company, which became Brookville Equipment Corp. in 1998, still builds small locomotives and also manufactures rapid-transit cars and, since the 2010s, builds and rebuilds heavy-duty diesel-electric freight and passenger locomotives. As of 2022, its new locomotive offerings include the BL36PH streamlined (semi-monocoque)

passenger locomotive and dual-service BL20GH road-switcher.

Electro-Motive Corp. (EMC)
Electro-Motive Division of General Motors (EMD)
General Motors Locomotive Group (GMLG)
Electro-Motive Diesel/ Progress Rail Services
General Motors Diesel Division (GMDD, Canada)

The Electro-Motive Corp. (EMC) began by contracting construction of gas-electric motor cars (doodlebugs) by other companies in the early 1920s. The motor cars used GE electrical equipment, Winton engines, and carbodies built by St. Louis Car Co., Pullman, and others. General Motors purchased both EMC and the Winton Engine Co. in 1930, but kept them as separate entities. Together, the companies developed power cars for several high-speed passenger trains, notably the Union Pacific's M-10000 (the first internal-combustion streamliner, with a distillate engine) and Burlington Route's *Zephyr* (the first diesel streamliner) in 1934. Switch engines and

Baldwin road switchers were distinctive, with squared-off hood ends. Milwaukee Road No. 926 is a medium-horse-power 1,200-hp RS12 built in 1951. It has a steam generator in the high nose; the Milwaukee used the locomotive in passenger terminals. This one is in Minneapolis in 1967.

J. David Ingles

Electro-Motive sold more diesel-electrics through the 1980s than any other builder, and the company's FT, more than any other diesel, spelled the end for steam locomotives in North America. Minneapolis & St. Louis No. 545 is a three-unit (A-B-A) FT built in 1945.

Trains collection

stand-alone passenger locomotives followed. After having its first locomotives assembled by outside contractors, EMC completed its own plant in La Grange, Ill., in 1936.

General Motors merged Winton and EMC in 1941, and EMC became the Electro-Motive Division of GM, or EMD. By the end of World War II, EMD — led by its pioneering FT cab-unit road diesel (introduced in 1939) — had a huge lead in diesel market share, aided significantly by the War Production Board allowing EMD to be the only manufacturer to build road-freight locomotives during World War II. Even though EMD was late to produce a road switcher (1949's GP7), it quickly became one of the most popular locomotives ever built.

In 1950, GM opened a locomotive plant in London, Ontario: General Motors Diesel, Ltd. (GMD). The company, later renamed General Motors Diesel Division (GMDD), built EMD-design locomotives for Canadian railroads and other export buyers.

EMD began losing market share to General Electric by the late 1970s, and GE eclipsed EMD in sales in 1987. General

Motors shifted all EMD assembly operations to the London plant in 1988, although many locomotives were also assembled at other independent and railroad-owned shops on a contract basis. At the same time, EMD and GMDD officially became General Motors Locomotive Group (GMLG).

In 2005, GM sold GMLG to Greenbriar Equity Group and Berkshire Partners. The new owners created a new company, Electro-Motive Diesel. In 2010, the new EMD was sold to Progress Rail Services, a subsidiary of Caterpillar. Electro-Motive Diesel now has its headquarters, as well as engineering and parts manufacturing facilities, at McCook, Ill., with locomotive assembly in Muncie, Ind.

Fairbanks-Morse (FM) Canadian Locomotive Co. (CLC)

Fairbanks-Morse was a late entrant to diesel locomotive manufacturing. The company's unique opposed-piston (OP) diesel engine was first used in naval vessels in the early 1930s. Looking for other applications for the design, F-M turned

to railroads. In 1939, the company's OP engines were used in six railcars built by St. Louis Car Co. for the Southern Railway.

The company's first diesel switchers appeared in 1944, with cab units and road-switchers following shortly after World War II. Although the OP engine offered more power compared to a similar-size conventional diesel, maintenance problems and costs countered the OP engine's power and efficiency gains. The company's locomotive sales slowed during the 1950s, with the last

F-M domestic diesel built in 1958 and the last export order completed in 1963.

The company was perhaps best known for its huge six-axle Train Master (H24-66) road switcher, a 2,400-hp design that was, at its introduction in 1953, the most powerful single-engine road diesel in service. However, F-M's road locomotives suffered from a variety of mechanical and reliability issues. The company's switchers, however, earned a reputation as dependable, hard-pulling engines, with many lasting into the 1970s.

Although the builder has passed through changes of ownership, EMD — now Electro-Motive Diesel — continues to manufacture locomotives. The latest is the Tier-4 compliant SD70ACe-T4, a 4,400-hp, AC-motor locomotive. *Cody Grivno*

The 2,400-hp Fairbanks-Morse Train Master (H24-66) was the highest-horse-power single-engine diesel locomotive when introduced in 1953. It remains an iconic loco-motive, even though sales (127 total) did not match the horsepower or hype. Virginian had the largest fleet, with 25. Number 51 was built in 1954.
Trains collection

General Electric's 1960 introduction of a high-horsepower road switcher — the 2,500-hp U25B — soon vaulted the company into second-place in the diesel market ahead of Alco. Chicago, Burlington & Quincy No. 100 is on its way to delivery to the railroad in September 1964.

Louis A. Marre

Locomotives were built at F-M's plant in Beloit, Wis., except for the company's big six-axle Erie-Built cab units. These locomotives were built at General Electric's Erie, Pa., plant, earning them their nickname. (They were built before GE introduced its own line of heavy diesel-electrics.) Fairbanks-Morse-design locomotives were also built at F-M's Canadian licensee, Canadian Locomotive Co., in Kingston, Ontario. In 1950 Fairbanks-Morse acquired CLC; the Kingston plant produced F-M-design diesels until about 1956.

General Electric (GE)
Wabtec

General Electric was a leader in the development of electric railway equipment, building traction motors, generators, and control equipment for streetcars and electric railways in the late 1800s. The company began supplying electrical equipment to gas-electric motor car manufacturers in the 1920s. GE was an early partner with locomotive builder Alco and diesel engine maker Ingersoll-Rand, building heavy electric locomotives with Alco and diesel-electric boxcab switchers with Alco/I-R in the 1920s and providing equipment (and

General Electric's Dash-7 line, introduced in 1976, debuted a number of electrical and engine upgrades compared to the former Universal line. The 3,000-hp C30-7, including Burlington Northern No. 5034, earned a reputation as a rugged heavy-haul locomotive and was popular in coal-train service.

David A. Bontrager

assembly) for Electro-Motive and others in the 1930s.

General Electric had its own line of small- to medium-size switching and industrial diesel locomotives (notably its 44-ton and 70-ton models) beginning in the 1930s, and from 1940 to 1953 partnered with Alco to produce road freight and passenger locomotives.

After dissolving its partnership with Alco, General Electric entered the domestic heavy-duty freight locomotive market on its own in 1959 when it introduced its Universal (U) series of road switchers, starting with the 2,500-hp, four-axle U25B, followed soon by the six-axle U25C. The first production models appeared in 1961, and within three years GE had surpassed Alco to become the No. 2 locomotive builder in the country. By 1968, GE's market share was 33% and growing. Numerous improvements to GE's line led to increased sales, and by 1987, its Dash-7 and later Dash-8 series of locomotives pushed General Electric past EMD to become the largest locomotive builder in North America.

In 2019, Wabtec (successor to Westinghouse) acquired GE's locomotive business (GE Transportation), with GE Transportation becoming a division of Wabtec. Locomotive production moved from Erie, Pa., to Fort Worth, Texas, with engines manufactured at Grove City, Pa.

Lima-Hamilton

Lima Locomotive Works was the third-largest steam builder, but by the 1930s was regarded as the most innovative, and the company was building the most technologically advanced steam locomotives of the period. No steam innovations, however, would slow the industry's move to diesels, and Lima (named after its home city of Lima, Ohio) built its last steam locomotive in 1949.

Lima was too slow to recognize the inevitable and entered the diesel market too late to capture anything but token business. In 1947 Lima merged with General Machinery Corporation of Hamilton, Ohio, taking advantage of that company's diesel engine designs, to form the Lima-Hamilton Corp. The merged company didn't release a production diesel locomotive until 1949, then built just 175 of them into 1951 when it merged with rival Baldwin Locomotive Works to form the Baldwin-Lima-Hamilton Corp.; the Lima-Hamilton line of diesels was discontinued.

Although Lima was known for innovations in steam power, the company was late in entering the diesel market, building just 175 diesel-electrics before merging with Baldwin. Lima-Hamilton switchers looked similar to contemporary Alco switchers but with more squared-off hood angles. *Lima-Hamilton*

Caltrain No. 926 is an MPXpress MP36PH-3C, built by MPI. The modern 3,600-hp passenger locomotive is powered by an EMD 645F3B engine with a separate head-end power engine/alternator.
Brian Solomon

MotivePower, Inc. (MPI) Morrison-Knudsen (MK, MK Rail)

MotivePower, Inc. (MPI) is a wholly owned subsidiary of Wabtec that rebuilds and repowers locomotives and also offers its own catalog of locomotives, led by the MPXpress series of passenger diesels (since 2003). The company traces its history to Morrison-Knudsen, which established its MK Rail subsidiary to build and rebuild diesel-electric locomotives in Boise, Idaho, starting in 1972. In 1996, the company became MotivePower Industries' Boise Locomotive division. The company merged with Westinghouse Air Brake (Wabco) in 1999, becoming the company's MotivePower, Inc., division. Wabtec, Wabco's successor, closed the MPI Boise plant in 2020 at the time of its merger with

GE Transportation. MPI production was shifted to the former GE locomotive plant in Erie, Pa.

Siemens Mobility

Siemens Mobility is the locomotive-building company of Siemens AG, with a manufacturing plant in Sacramento, Calif. (The parent company's corporate headquarters is in Munich, Germany.) Siemens has been involved in electric railroad technology and development internationally since the 1800s, and Siemens was an innovator in developing AC traction-motor technology in the 1970s and 1980s. The company began producing its own line of locomotives in the 2000s; the latest is the Siemens Charger line of streamlined passenger diesels, produced since 2016.

An Amtrak Siemens ALC-42 leads a train shortly after entering service in February 2022. The 4,200-hp, Tier-4-compliant locomotive is one of the models in the Siemens Charger line of monocoque-design streamlined passenger diesels. *David Lassen*

BIBLIOGRAPHY

BOOKS

The Contemporary Diesel Spotter's Guide, by Louis A. Marre and Paul K. Withers. Withers Publishing, 2000.

The Diesel Builders: Fairbanks-Morse and Lima-Hamilton, by John F. Kirkland. Interurban Press, 1985.

The Diesel Builders, Volume 2: American Locomotive Company and Montreal Locomotive Works, by John F. Kirkland. Interurban Press, 1989.

The Diesel Builders, Volume 3: Baldwin Locomotive Works, by John F. Kirkland. Interurban Press, 1994.

Diesel-Electric Locomotive. Diesel Publications, Inc., 1946.

The Diesel From D to L, by Vernon L. Smith. Kalmbach Publishing Co., 1979.

Diesels from Eddystone, by Gary W. Dolzall and Stephen F. Dolzall. Kalmbach Publishing Co., 1984.

The Dilworth Story, by Franklin M. Reck. McGraw-Hill/Electro-Motive Division, 1954.

Doodlebug Country, by Edmund Keilty. Interurban Press, 1982.

Electric Locomotives, by Brian Solomon. MBI Publishing, 2003.

Electrification by GE. Central Electric Railfans' Association, Bulletin 116, 1976.

EMD Locomotives, by Brian Solomon. Voyageur Press, 2006.

Evolution of the American Diesel Locomotive, by J. Parker Lamb. Indiana University Press, 2007.

GE Evolution Locomotives, by Sean Graham-White. Voyageur Press, 2007.

General Motors Phenomenal SD40 Series Diesel-Electric Locomotives, by James W. Kerr. Delta Publications, 2004.

Guide to North American Diesel Locomotives, by Jeff Wilson. Kalmbach Publishing Co., 2017.

Illustrated Treasury of the American Locomotive Company. Delta Publications, 1980.

Model Railroader Cyclopedia — Volume 2: Diesel Locomotives, compiled by Bob Hayden. Kalmbach Publishing Co., 1980.

The Second Diesel Spotter's Guide, by Jerry A. Pinkepank. Kalmbach Publishing Co., 1973.

PERIODICALS

"The ABCs, and Ds, of EMD's 567 Prime Mover," by David Lustig, *Trains,* October 2002, p. 24.

"AC Rules!" by Greg McDonnell, *Locomotive, Trains* special edition, annual 2020, p.60.

"AC Rules, DC Drools," by Chris Guss, *Trains,* June 2019, p. 14.

"After PTC," by Malcolm Kenton, *Trains,* February 2021, p. 34.

"Alco RS1: The Original Road Switcher," *Extra 2200 South,* Part 1, July-August-September 1976, p. 18; Part 2, October-November-December 1976, p. 19.

"All About Fs," by Dan Dover, *Extra 2200 South,* January 1970, p. 19.

"All About SWs," by Dan Dover, *Extra 2200 South,* July-August 1973, p. 20.

"Amtrak's New Electric Workhorse" (ACS-64), by Bob Johnston, *Trains,* January 2015, p. 24.

"Builders in Tier 4 Territory," by Chris Guss, *Trains,* December 2015, p. 18.

"Cab Safety Evolves," by Chris Guss, *Trains,* December 2013, p. 18.

"Dash 3: What Is It?" by David Lustig, *Trains,* October 2010, p. 17.

"Dash 8: The Diesel that Dethroned EMD," by Steve Gerbracht and Greg McDonnell, *Locomotive, Trains* special edition, annual 2022, p. 68.

"Diesel Dynasty: Exploring the origins of the GE 7FDL Diesel Engine," by Michael E. Iden, *Locomotive, Trains* special edition, annual 2021, p. 22.

"Distributed Power's Wonder Years," by Ron Flanary, *Trains,* September 2010, p. 34.

"Dynamic Braking: How it Works, Why it Works," by David Lustig, *Trains,* December 2002, p. 30.

"E8/E9 Roster," by Dan Dover, *Extra 2200 South,* November-December 1973, p. 15.

"Early Geeps," by Don Dover, *Extra 2200 South,* October-November-December 1971, p. 7.

"EMD 265H Diesel Engine," *Trains,* October 2002, p. 48.

"The EMD Epoch," by Robert S. McGonigal, Greg McDonnell, *EMD At 100, Trains* special issue 2022, p. 10.

"EMD Rising," by David Lustig and Fred W. Frailey, *Trains,* January 2011, p.24.

"EMD's F45 and FP45," by Paul K. Withers, *Diesel Era,* Volume 10, No. 2, p. 11.

"EMD's SD70ACe and SD70M-2," by Sean Graham-White, *Diesel Era,* August 2007, p. 15.

"The FDL Advantage," by Steve Gerbracht, *Locomotive, Trains* special edition, annual 2021, p. 22.

"Freight Train, Unbounded — Distributed Power: It's a Bigger Deal than you Think," by David Lustig, *Trains,* September 2010, p. 22.

"A Fresh Look at Adhesion," *Extra 2200 South,* February-March 1969, p. 22.

"From the Halls of Baldwin," *Trains,* May 1962, p. 42.

"GE AC4400 Data Sheet," by Sean Graham-White, *Trains,* March 2004, p. 46.

"General Electric: A Prophecy Fulfilled," by Greg McDonnell, *Locomotive, Trains* special edition, annual 2022, p. 58.

"Genesis: Amtrak's New Breed," by Bob Johnston, *Trains,* September 1993, p. 36.

"GEVO vs. ACe," by Jeffrey Capps, *Model Railroader,* November 2004, p. 68.

"Helpers: How They Work, From Double-Heading to Distributed Power," by Jack Wheelihan, *Trains,* August 2001, p. 42.

"Helpers: Where They Are — Manned Helpers vs. Distributed Power," by Tom Murray, *Trains,* August 2001, p. 52.

"High-horsepower Homogeny," by Chris Guss, *Trains,* November 2018, p. 14.

"How the 'Home of the Diesel Locomotive' Builds Diesels," by Jerry A. Pinkepank, *EMD At 100, Trains* special issue 2022, p. 44.

"Internal Combustion Locomotives and Vehicles," by S.M. Vauclain, *Baldwin Locomotives Magazine,* July 1926, p. 43.

"Lash 'Em Up! How to Mate Miscellaneous Makes and Models," by Jerry A. Pinkepank, *Trains,* December 1968, p. 45.

"Letting the Cat out of the Bag" (SD70ACe), by Chris Guss, Jim Wrinn, *Trains,* March 2013, p. 50.

"The Little Locomotive that Did" (F40PH), by Sean Graham-White and Lester Weil, *Trains,* December 1999, p. 52.

"Locomotive Automation: The Changing Role of the Engineer in the Cab," by Chris Guss, *Trains,* April 2020, p. 16.

"Locomotive of the Future: EMD's SD70ACe," by Mark W. Hemphill, *Trains,* February 2004, p. 38.

"A New Dress for Opposed Pistons," by David P. Morgan, *Trains,* December 1948, p. 40 (reprinted in *Classic Trains,* Spring 2005, p. 52).

"PTC Onboard," by Chris Guss, *Trains,* December 2019, p. 16.

"Real Horse Power: The Diesels that Move Norfolk Southern's Trains," by Chris Guss, *Horse Power, Trains* special edition annual No. 2, 2022, p. 20.

"Taking On Tier 4," by Greg McDonnell, *Trains,* November 2012, p. 21.

"Those Early Es," by Louis A. Marre, *Extra 2200 South,* April 1968, p. 19.

"Those Red Diamond Diesels" (Lima-Hamilton), by Jerry A. Pinkepank and George J. Sennhauser, *Trains,* November 1963, p. 26.

"Turbocharged," by Chris Guss, *Trains,* November 2019, p. 16.

"20/20: The Age of Change," by Michael E. Iden, *Locomotive, Trains* special edition, annual 2020, p. 10.

"Understanding Freight Train Air Brakes," by Steve Wildermuth, *Diesel Era,* May/June 2014, p. 50.

"Wheel Slip Detection," by Joe McNulty, *Extra 2200 South,* January 1970, p. 28.

MISC. SOURCES

Locomotive Cyclopedia (Simmons-Boardman), various issues.

Operating manuals, various models and manufacturers.

Manufacturer specification sheets and promotional materials, various.

Modern Locomotive Brake Equipment, Performance and Characteristics, Descriptive Catalog No. 2052-1, Westinghouse Air Brake Co., 1945.

26-L Brake Equipment for Locomotives, Instruction Pamphlet No. 5071-6, Westinghouse Air Brake Co., 1958.

WEBSITES

American Rails, american-rails.com

Association of American Railroads, aar.org

The Baldwin Diesel Zone, baldwindiesels.railfan.net

Brookville Equipment Corp., brookvillecorp.com

The Diesel Shop, thedieselshop.us

Electro-Motive Diesel/Progress Rail, progressrail.com

Federal Railroad Administration, railroads.dot.gov

Motive Power Inc., motive-power.com

Siemens, mobility.siemens.com

Trains magazine, trains.com

UtahRails.net

Wabtec, wabteccorp.com

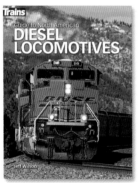
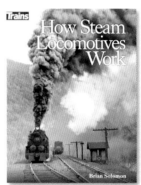
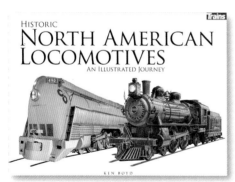
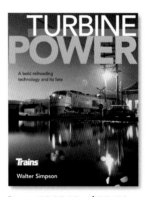